Advance Praise for
Mindful Eating for The Beloved Community

"Success, in every realm of life depends on being mindful.
But what must come first each and every day? Mindful eating,
the essential aspect that enables us to conquer all!"

EDWARD C. WASHINGTON
Corporate AD Manager | American Express Global Corporate Services

Food is meant to nurture, to be a source for enjoyment and,
most importantly, to sustain the body and
the soul for the journey of life."

EXECUTIVE CHEF JASON FLAGG
*Assistant Director of Food & Nutrition | Langone Orthopedic Hospital
at NYU*

"As a 20-year veteran of the kitchen and
Food Network Grand Champion,
I think these powerful stories are by far the best collection
to illustrate the connection between health and wealth and
the mindset needed to perform at the highest level."

CELEBRITY CHEF DANIELLE SAUNDERS

mindful eating
for the beloved community

mindful eating
for the beloved community
food for social justice

ARCH STREET PRESS
BRYN MAWR

Arch Street Press

Bryn Mawr, PA · USA

First Arch Street Press edition January 2018

ARCH STREET PRESS, ARCH ST. PRESS and colophon are registered trademarks of Arch Street Press.

For information about special discounts for bulk and nonprofit purchases, please contact Arch Street Press: sales@archstreetpress.org.

Cover design by Kathy McLaughlin

Library of Congress Cataloging-in-Publication Data is available.

ISBN: 978-1-938798-17-7
ISBN: 978-1-938798-19-1 (e-book)

"Our goal is to create a beloved community,
and this will require a qualitative change in our souls
as well as a quantitative change in our lives."

—Martin Luther King, Jr.

"Dr. King's Beloved Community is a global vision
in which all people can share in the wealth of the earth.
In the Beloved Community, poverty, hunger
and homelessness will not be tolerated
because international standards of human decency
will not allow it.
Racism and all forms of discrimination, bigotry
and prejudice will be replaced by an all-inclusive spirit
of sisterhood and brotherhood."

—The King Center

ACKNOWLEDGMENTS

The inspiration for *Mindful Eating for The Beloved Community* in great part came from my experience as a Fellow with the Kellogg Foundation. Throughout my three-year journey I became a part of an important and powerful network that included David Castro, who introduced and coached me on systems thinking, and Chris Block, who introduced me to the practice of meditation. M. von Nkosi taught me the significance of preserving cultural heritage and Kevin Fong exposed me to balance training by means of the Five Elements.

I was inspired by Mark Bertolini, the CEO of Aetna at the time, and Aetna Vice President Floyd Green, to explore the benefits of mindfulness and being present. All of the contributors who signed on to the project (and even those who couldn't sign on but encouraged the movement) helped make the idea of *Mindfulness for The Beloved Community* a reality. I would also like to acknowledge the first organization that endorsed the project, Blacks in Government (BIG). I want to thank Dr. Doris Sartor—President of BIG—and Bettie Hudson—Chair, Health and Wellness (BIG)—for their validation and belief that this is the right moment to address the issues of food insecurity, food as social justice and the need for the practice of mindfulness in everything we do.

Our publishing partner, Arch Street Press, provided outstanding support for the project. Dave Castro, Ann Black and Jim Warner worked on every aspect of the book and the larger project from creating a website to developing a technology strategy to measure the metrics and collect critical data to help us grow a national movement. And last but not least in importance are the wonderful and dynamic contributors from all walks of The Beloved Community. Their stories will make you think, feel, long for—and most importantly—strive to sit mindfully at the table of brotherhood and sisterhood, a table that serves health and justice for all.

—*Alex Askew*

TABLE OF CONTENTS

FOREWORD

Eating... it's such a natural process for us humans.

Food is what keeps us alive and satisfied, fills a void and connects us. Food matters because it helps to reduce suffering, while nurturing and healing. It often makes us happy. Frankly, food is medicine.

Mindfulness forces us to focus our awareness on the present moment and not dwell on the past or future.

When Alex Askew—cofounder of BCA Global (formerly the Black Culinarian Alliance)—invited me to write this foreword, I said "yes" because I have seen the tireless work of his organization, with its dedication and commitment to educating and creating opportunities for young minority students seeking careers in the culinary and hospitality industries. Moreover, this project is about issues near and dear to my heart. It is about eating, mindfulness, food and the beloved community.

This book is borne out of a national collaboration that brought chefs, agriculturalists, social-justice activists and meditation experts together within a powerful storytelling forum. Each collaborator offers an abundance of strategies to rebuild the connections between diet, culture, faith, the environment and community well-being, with an emphasis on the deep connection between mindful eating, social justice and sustainability. Their stories elegantly demonstrate that some of the traditional meanings and emotions associated with eating have eroded over time, and that it is indeed time to start a conversation about how to reclaim them.

As a healthcare professional with a lengthy career in nutrition within healthcare settings, I know that these days, eating well and eating mindfully don't always go hand in hand. Health disparities based on race, income and ethnicity do exist in our communities. Furthermore, there is a mountain of evidence confirming that people living in poorer neighborhoods are less likely to have easy access to a wide variety of high-quality fresh produce and other healthy foods. What's striking is that convenience stores often used by people living in poorer communities may charge more, and the food is generally of a lesser quality.

This lack of access to healthy food options results in the consumption of fewer nutrient-dense foods, fruits, vegetables and whole grains, fostered by a food environment that places the poor at highest risk for unhealthful diets and obesity—the fastest-growing cause of disease and death in America. This crisis and the rise of other degenerative diseases are fueled by sedentary lifestyles with less physical activity, and overconsumption of foods high in sodium, fat and sugar.

The plethora of unhealthy messages that our children are exposed to through advertising is a leading cause of unhealthy food consumption; many of these ads promote food to children showing unhealthy eating behaviors with seemingly positive outcomes. *Mindful Eating for The Beloved Community* bridges the gap between what's wrong and how we can begin to make it right. The stories are powerful and the messages they deliver are crystal clear.

In the pages ahead you'll be introduced to a wide range of contributors who have dedicated their lives to mindful eating. **Alex Askew** compares the unhealthy eating lifestyle with the risk behavior associated with casual sex; **Njathi Kabui** provides a historical context for the current food climate in our communities; **Anzia Bennett** explores the individual benefits enjoyed by mindful eaters and how they impact the community at large; and **Brealynn Lee** reviews the importance of pre/post-natal nutrition for the new mother.

In addition, **Michael Easterling's** thought-provoking story on the value of urban agriculture as a community-development strategy points out that fresh fruits and vegetables are not available in much of the urban core, but processed foods, alcohol and tobacco are everywhere. Blacks and Latinos in American cities are far more likely to live in a food desert than any other group.

Creative solutions are needed to facilitate healthy food access, entrepreneurial opportunities, environmental sustainability and stronger communities. Better farming will enhance the safety and security of our food supply while improving the environment. There is also a huge opportunity to engage senior communities, youth and neighborhoods of color.

Michael points out that there is a need for innovative approaches to urban farming that can maximize production on limited space. By reimagining what our food supply could look like, we have the opportunity to make dramatic changes to the health, well-being and economic state of local communities. Rather than a centralized food-supply system, what if we went back to our roots and created self-sufficient farming cultures in individual communities?

Ultimately, everyone stands to benefit from the opportunities of local food sourcing. Community-based agriculture cultivates interpersonal relationships among residents, improves individual and public health, provides rewarding opportunities to connect and give back, and leads to overall environmental sustainability. As we move forward, consider this crucial question: Do we want to be a society controlled by centralized farming or do we want to implement strategies to support and develop a local and sustainable approach?

Contributor **Victor Ruiz** well understands the impact of families eating together from his personal experience; he speaks to its psychological significance and draws a sharp contrast between his dining experiences growing up versus contemporary practices. When his mom got her first job outside of the home, food was more likely to be eaten alone and in front of the TV or on the run, and hot breakfasts eventually became cold cereal.

Victor points out the overwhelming evidence supporting the benefits of family meal time. As a parent himself, creating his own family traditions became more difficult as life got busier and he missed dinners with his own family. One solution is that we create more mealtime experiences for our children and families in schools, daycares, summer meal programs and churches. Schools can invite parents and community members to eat meals with students and engage in meaningful exchanges. We must also be ambassadors of Dr. Martin Luther King, Jr.'s vision of the beloved community that, in its simplest form, is made up of people loving each other and expressing that love through acts of kindness. It starts at home.

Chris Block explores the yoga of eating and explains that, in today's society, we often find ourselves rushing from one task to the next, one meeting to another, trying to get all of our tasks checked off the list. We rarely take the time to stop and focus on what is going on in the present moment, yet this connection to the present allows us to have a deeper bond with life and the world that surrounds us. Priorities and goals then come into focus, creativity begins to flow and relationships can flourish.

Chris points out that mindfulness is a way to keep polishing the window of our lives, allowing us to actually see the possibilities before us to live life fully, experience our families completely and have fulfilling careers. Further, he shares tools and practices to help make us much more attuned to the state of our interior condition.

Mindful eating is one such practice that can help us tune in to overlooked aspects of our lives due to difficulties or endless to-do lists. By taking the time to examine food's physical properties and using our senses to appreciate the effects that it has on our minds and bodies, we can begin to peel away the layers that may well have been clouding our perceptions. When we slow down and actually pay attention, we are able to see and hear what we've been missing with a clarity not otherwise possible.

This book significantly helps to deepen our understanding of mindful eating. I applaud the contributors for sharing their personal experiences and perspectives, and offering common-sense approaches that we can adopt with tangible and life-giving benefits.

Eating is a profoundly social urge; as a society we are obsessed with food that represents an occasion for sharing and giving, and for the expression of kindness. Food is a beacon—a symbol of love, security and sociability. Yet we must eat mindfully. We are past the tipping point and have to teach our communities to enjoy healthy food. Let's not stand by without taking action. Lead by example; become part of this conversation in homes, communities, leadership groups and board rooms.

By opening these pages, you have started a mindful and indelible journey. Read on!

Veronica McLymont,
PhD, RD, CDN, CPC

INTRODUCING THE CONCEPT
OF THE MINDFUL MEAL
Becoming the Change That We Wish to See in the World

During our work on *Mindful Eating for The Beloved Community,* people interested in our efforts often asked us a challenging question: "How do you intend to measure your impact?" We understood the importance of this question, because we live in a world where talk, dialogue and debate often doesn't lead to action and change. Yet progress and social justice depend on action as their lifeblood.

What is the real difference that we think this book will make? Every person on earth stays alive by eating a certain number of meals per day and week. How many of those meals are mindful? Too few. And that is what leads our beloved community to malnutrition and the host of health challenges and missed opportunities that result when we eat carelessly. The solution is straightforward: increase the number of mindful meals consumed every day. Every such meal accomplished is a victory for the individual, family and community who enjoys it. How do we define it? That too is straightforward; a mindful meal...

1. Includes a sincere prayer/expression of gratitude;
2. Includes at least 30 minutes for meaningful personal connection;
3. Includes at least three healthy ingredients from our healthy-foods list;
4. Does not include any ingredients from our unhealthy-foods list;
5. Includes up to 500 calories of nutrition;
6. Is a meaningful work of culinary art that pleases the senses; and
7. Builds a sense of understanding and community among those who consume it.

Our shared path to real, measurable impact is simple: Increase the number of mindful meals each week and reduce number of non-mindful meals. The best way is to join the Mindful Eating Social

Network, through which you earn a mindful-meal credit whenever you provide a mindful meal to another person, who acknowledges receiving it through the network software. A meal is scored as mindful when it meets the above criteria. The person providing the meal also receives a 1- to 5-star review to let others in the network know whether he or she is a good partner to share mindful meals. Each earned credit can then be spent consuming another mindful meal offered by a friend within the network. You can always earn credits by introducing new people to the mindful-meal network and having them join. Through this mindful-meal-sharing platform, you will also save financial resources, empowering your body, spirit and finances in a synergistic approach. The network will also provide you with on-going opportunities to learn more about mindfulness, culinary arts, nutrition and social justice. Find the network and our healthy foods list at www.belovedmindfuleating.org.

Now it's up to you. Be the change.

David M. Castro

DON'T TREAT FOOD LIKE CASUAL SEX
by Chef Alex Askew

Most of us are familiar with the concept of casual sex. It's so much a part of our culture that an urban dictionary defines it as junk-food sex. The effects of casual sex include unhealthy relationships, a malnourished emotional life and other self-destructive behaviors. The major risk factor is having an encounter in which you have eliminated the potential of engaging in a long-term relationship. There is a peculiar parallel with the interaction between people and people, and people and food. McDonald's, Chinese takeout and Taco Bell are like apps such as Tinder and Grindr that make having a quick-as-possible encounter even more accessible. You meet, hook up and then go your separate ways. It's analogous to the drive-up window at McDonald's or Chinese delivery. Junk food is like casual sex. It doesn't seem so bad in the moment but you aren't doing yourself any favors if it's the only thing you eat.

Those slices of pizza or 4 a.m. visits to the diner after a late night of drinking (most of us have been there) temporarily satisfy our hunger and fill our stomachs. But the next day we often feel guilty for our overindulgences. The same goes for casual sex. Something is temporarily satisfied, yet a steady diet of casual encounters can damage our self-respect.

Fast food and processed food are bad for us. Habitually eating them will damage our health over time. The occasional high-fat meal won't hurt; however, eating it often will. There's no disputing that a diet high in fat, sugar, salt and calories will make you unhealthy and lacks nutritional value. But junk food tastes so good that we just can't get enough! Have you ever tried to have just two potato chips? Your body typically responds in a loud voice: "Are you kidding me?" What tastes good about junk food are the chemical combinations used to produce taste.

Some people (like me) know the possibility that the whole bag will be eaten and I rarely have those kinds of food in my house. Junk food, like casual sex, is not going to do anything to bolster your self-respect. We have to develop self-control to resist the appeal of that which is bad for us.

In an essay for *Psychology Today*, Dr. Aaron Ben-Zeév stated, "In comparing junk food to junk sex, intimacy might be considered to be the 'nutritional value' of sex.... Intimacy involves a feeling of closeness and belonging, which are vital of healthy sex."[1] This has a clear bearing on how a healthy food relationship can be developed when you care about yourself. It's not about instant gratification but long-term satisfaction. Most times instant gratification is irresistible; we care neither what it takes to get it nor about the repercussions. What goes through our mind and soul afterward? Do we feel gross? Are there regrets? I had that experience many times back in college with late nights at White Castle. Talk about regret! But over and over, we find ourselves in the same situation and soon feel that we don't care much about ourselves, with a loss of self-esteem particularly compared with those who eat right and take care of their body. This junk-food sex can lead to addiction without our even recognizing that it's happening. As with all things, balance is key.

Approximately 55% of U.S. adults are considered overweight. For some African Americans, a family tradition of soul food may pose a problem for today's less-active lifestyle. Soul foods traditionally depend on fat, sugar and sodium for their flavor, and regular consumption of this type of food can easily contribute to obesity, which is closely related to a long list of serious health problems such as type 2 diabetes, high blood pressure and cancer.

Data shows that the urban community typically chooses items such as fried chicken, barbecued ribs, cornbread, sweet-potato pie, collard greens and fruit-flavored drinks much more than in more affluent areas. Lactose intolerance is also more common in the urban community, resulting in a lower intake of dairy food. While food habits have changed throughout the years, there are still food-preparation practices that persist within the urban community; frying, for example, is more popular than boiling or baking foods.

The lack of local access to healthy foods makes it difficult for families who remain in low-income urban communities to maintain a well-balanced, nutritious diet. With limited transportation options, they must resort to purchasing unhealthy foods from nearby fast-food restaurants or local corner stores. Though more convenient,

1   https://www.psychologytoday.com/blog/in-the-name-love/201306/is-junk-sex-bad-junk-food

DON'T TREAT FOOD LIKE CASUAL SEX

they offer fewer healthy foods, are poorly maintained and charge higher prices, sometimes as much as 50% more than supermarkets. Their selection consists mainly of canned and processed foods and very little, if any, fresh meat and produce. A diet poor in fruits and vegetables increases the risk of diabetes, heart disease, cancer and other illnesses that disproportionately affect people of color. Poor dietary behaviors also contribute to the obesity epidemic, which is increasing at an alarming rate nationwide.

Good nutrition is an important part of leading a healthy lifestyle. Combined with physical activity, your diet can help you reach and maintain a healthy weight, reduce your risk of chronic diseases and promote your overall health. This naturally leads to healthier communities. The risk factors for chronic diseases like hypertension and type 2 diabetes are increasingly seen in younger ages. Dietary habits established in childhood often carry into adulthood, so teaching children how to eat well will help them stay healthy throughout their lives. Food is the source of energy for all of our bodily functions, and directly affects how our bodies and minds function in every stage of life. Proteins, carbohydrates and fats are the building blocks of energy. After ingestion, carbohydrates are broken down into glucose, which provides raw energy that is either used immediately or stored in the muscles for later use. Complex carbohydrates like whole grains, vegetables and fruits provide a balance of calories and nutrients, whereas simple carbs such as sugar and white flour are high in calories and low in nutrients, making them a poor choice for energy production.

Health on a Budget
Grains are typically cheap; most can be purchased in season for a good price and even bought frozen at a high quality. A few steps can help you make easy, healthy family meals on a budget. Find time to plan and prepare healthy meals each week. Use the time you save to enjoy your family. Plan the meals, snacks and beverages that you will serve throughout the week. Write down a list of foods needed to prepare meals or keep the list in a wallet, purse or mobile phone. Focus your budget on foods that are healthier for your family such as vegetables, fruits, whole grains, dairy and proteins. Look in newspapers or weekly store flyers to find sales and coupons for foods that you need. Join a store's bonus or reward-card program to receive

more savings. Visit the store's customer-service desk or website for information about how to sign up. Choose foods that cost less all year long. Beans and eggs are low-cost and healthy protein foods. Frozen vegetables like spinach and green beans are also low-cost options. Stock your kitchen. Select foods that you can make and serve quickly on busy days, such as canned beans and fish, low-sodium vegetables and soups, whole-grain pasta, brown rice and quick-cooking oats.

Importance of Eating Grains

Studies show that eating whole grains instead of refined grains lowers the risk of many chronic diseases. While benefits are most pronounced for those consuming at least three servings daily, some studies show reduced risks from as little as one serving. Every whole grain in your diet helps. Of course, these benefits are most pronounced in the context of an overall healthy diet. It's also important to remember that some whole-grain foods are healthier than others, such as brown rice, quinoa, wheat berries and whole-grain pasta. Processed grains should be eaten less often. The benefits of whole grains most documented by repeated studies include reduced risk of stroke by 30–36%, type 2 diabetes by 21–30%, heart disease by 25–28%, better weight maintenance, reduced risk of asthma, healthier carotid arteries, reduction of inflammatory diseases, lower risk of colorectal cancer, healthier blood-pressure levels, and less gum disease and tooth loss.

An excellent example of a versatile grain is quinoa—one of the world's most popular health foods. It is gluten-free, high in protein and one of the few plant foods that contain all nine essential amino acids. It is also high in fiber, magnesium, B vitamins, iron, potassium, calcium, phosphorus, vitamin E and various beneficial antioxidants.

Quinoa is a grain crop grown for its edible seeds and was an important crop for the Inca Empire. They referred to it as the "mother of all grains" and believed it to be sacred. It has been consumed for thousands of years in South America, although it only became trendy and reached superfood status a few years ago. These days, you can find quinoa and products made with it all over the world, especially in health-food stores and restaurants that emphasize natural foods.

The health effects of real foods go far beyond the vitamins and minerals. These include interesting molecules called flavonoids, which are plant antioxidants that have been shown to have all sorts of beneficial effects on health. Two flavonoids that have been particularly well studied are quercetin and kaempferol, that are found in large amounts in quinoa. In fact, the quercetin content of quinoa is even higher than in typical high-quercetin foods like cranberries. These important molecules have been shown to have anti-inflammatory, antiviral, anticancer and antidepressant effects in animal studies.

Quinoa is also much higher in fiber than most grains, with numerous studies showing that soluble fiber can help reduce blood-sugar levels, lower cholesterol, increase fullness and help with weight loss. Quinoa is also gluten-free and perfect for people with gluten intolerance. Many researchers have been looking at quinoa as a suitable ingredient in gluten-free diets for people who don't want to give up staples like breads and pasta. Studies have shown that by using quinoa instead of typical gluten-free ingredients like refined tapioca, potato, corn and rice flour can dramatically increase a diet's nutrient and antioxidant value. It's also very high in protein with all of the essential amino acids, some of which are termed "essential" because we cannot produce them and need to get them through food. However, quinoa is an exception because it contains all of them. With eight grams of quality protein per cup, quinoa is an excellent plant-based protein source for vegetarians and vegans.

For the diabetic, quinoa has a low glycemic index, which is good for blood-sugar control. This index is a measure of how quickly foods raise blood-sugar levels. It is known that eating foods high on the glycemic index can stimulate hunger and contribute to obesity. Such foods have also been linked to many of the chronic Western diseases so common today, like type 2 diabetes and heart disease. Quinoa also has beneficial effects on metabolic health. Given the high amount of such nutrients, it makes sense that quinoa leads to improvements in metabolic health.

It's time for us to set a goal to transform our relationship with food. Radical adjustments don't work because we ask too much of ourselves too quickly; when we inevitably don't have instant success, we abandon the project. Begin your journey toward healthy eating by being mindful about why you eat, and where and when. Many apps can help you record what you are eating and, over time, you will see a pattern emerge. At the end of a month, decide one bad food habit to eliminate and replace it with something healthy. Then become mindful of the way you feel, after eating both poorly and wisely. Continue this process over a period of six months and watch your weight gradually decline, your energy gradually increase, your focus gradually improve and your mindset gradually sharpen.

Yes, mindful eating is a gradual—not casual—process, but the results both extend and last a lifetime.

MINDFUL MENU

Red Lentil Soup ♥ Light Cornbread

BLESSING
(Japanese Buddhist)

This food comes from the Earth and the Sky,
It is the gift of the entire universe
and the fruit of much hard work;
I vow to live a life which is worthy to receive it.

Red Lentil Soup | YIELDS 4 PORTIONS

INGREDIENTS

1½ cups red lentils

4 large carrots, peeled and chopped

1 red bell pepper, chopped

2 celery stalks, chopped

½ bunch of kale (about four leaves) with stems removed and chopped

2 russet potatoes, peeled and chopped

1 jalapeño, chopped (optional)

2 garlic cloves, pressed

½ onion, chopped

1 tsp salt

1 tsp parsley

½ tsp paprika

½ tsp oregano

½ tsp garlic salt

¼ tsp cayenne pepper

6½ cups vegetable stock

DIRECTIONS

1. Place all ingredients in a slow cooker and pour in vegetable stock.

2. Cook on high for five hours or low for eight hours (low is preferred).

3. Stir a few times throughout the cooking. If you like a more brothy soup, add in one to two cups of additional stock.

4. Serve with a dollop of sour cream and crusty bread on the side (optional).

Light Cornbread | YIELDS 8 PORTIONS

INGREDIENTS

¼ cups finely ground cornmeal

½ cup flour

1½ tsp baking powder

½ tsp baking soda

¼ tsp salt

1 tbsp unsalted butter or coconut oil, melted and cooled slightly

1 large egg, room temperature

1 tsp vanilla extract

½ cup plain nonfat Greek yogurt

2 tbsp honey

¼ cup nonfat milk

DIRECTIONS

1. Preheat the oven to 350°F, and coat an eight-inch-square pan with nonstick cooking spray.

2. In a medium bowl, whisk together the cornmeal, flour, baking powder, baking soda and salt. In a separate bowl, whisk together the butter, egg and vanilla. Stir in the Greek yogurt, mixing until no large lumps remain. Stir in the honey. Alternate between adding the cornmeal mixture and milk, beginning and ending with the cornmeal mixture, and stirring just until incorporated. (For best results, add the cornmeal mixture in three equal parts.)

3. Spread the batter into the prepared pan. Bake at 350° for 18 to 20 minutes or until the edges begin to turn golden and the center feels firm to the touch. Cool in the pan for at least 10 minutes before slicing and serving. (For the best texture, let it cool completely to room temperature.)

CULTIVATING A MINDFUL LIFESTYLE
by Jodi Brockington

I have suffered from a variety of health conditions, physical injuries and stress, and know many others who face similar issues. I finally learned truly and deeply the importance of living a mindful lifestyle, one in which my habits are healthy and consistent, and have a positive impact on both me and those around me. I also learned that what I put in my body directly affects how I will feel, and discovered how to be aware of what is happening inside and outside of myself. It comes down to what many of us have been told: We are what we eat and, importantly, what we do.

I firmly believe that slowing down to eat mindfully—with intention—is crucial to developing a healthy and happy relationship with the food that fuels us. It is also important to be mindful throughout the day: at work and with friends and family. Fortunately, there are many ways to work mindfulness into our daily routines, from eating, exercising and working to spending time with those about whom we care. The trick is to turn mindful living behaviors into daily rituals that are aligned with our values. It takes 21 days to create a habit and only seven days to break it.

It's much easier to exercise regularly when you enjoy what you're doing. Exercise is important for each of us; it makes us feel great and helps us stay healthy. Expand your definition of exercise beyond the usual and do what *actually* feels like fun and makes you happy. Put on music and dance in your living room, try a new class or experiment with a new style of yoga. You never know, maybe the high-intensity training of Tabata or indoor cycling will become your thing! Something's out there that will make you happy, while keeping you moving and healthy.

mind·ful·ness

ˈmīn(d)f(ə)lnəs/

noun

1. the quality or state of being conscious or aware of something. "Their mindfulness of the environment led them to conserve energy."

2. a mental state achieved by focusing one's awareness on the present moment, while calmly acknowledging and accepting one's thoughts, feelings and bodily sensations (often used as a therapeutic technique).

A mindful lifestyle means cultivating awareness. Being in tune with yourself and the world around you—and understanding how you relate to each—occurs when you are mindful. Once aware of your connection to the world, it's impossible to ever again ignore how your actions affect everything around you. Mindfulness isn't just a one-time decision to be conscious of your impact on the world; it's a lifestyle that forever shapes how you move and make decisions.

Mindfulness is the practice of becoming more aware of your body, thoughts and surroundings. It helps you to be more present and enjoy the now instead of worrying about what has happened in the past or what might happen in the future.

Seven Simple Shifts to Make Mindfulness Your Lifestyle
Observe your thoughts and feelings without judgment. This is probably one of the most challenging shifts to make because we *all* struggle with ignoring the judgments of others and engaging in negative self-talk.

Since childhood, I often found myself observing my thoughts and feelings around food. I have been a picky eater and should probably still have one of those divided plates that often appear at picnics or barbeques so that different foods do not touch and/or slide around the plate. My parents and family members believed that we had to eat everything on our plate. Also, they would use food as a bribe; dessert was withheld until I finished the main meal or I could not leave the table until that happened. My childhood experience with food has made me very mindful of the kind of food and portion sizes I eat.

1. Stay focused on the task at hand: Whatever you are doing, stay in that moment. Be fully present when you are visiting family or friends. Turn the cellphone off, and take time to listen and engage in meaningful conversations.

It is important to stay focused on the tasks at hand when you are cooking, following a recipe, trying to figure out how or if you could add something to make it taste even better, or simply when it is time to eat. Many people who have the privilege of sitting around the table to dine with family members use that time to connect with each other. Try not to rush through your meal. Enjoy each bite and the company of other people, or simply your own company. Be in that very moment with your food. Relish the flavors, the texture and the temperature.

2. Observe when your mind is in the past or future, and bring it back to the present.

We all have things from our past that come up, whether good or bad memories; think about why they are coming up for you at that time. Also, when considering the future, is it because you think that it will be better or do you fear the worst? Any of these thoughts limit your movement and beliefs. Acknowledge these moments in the present and move forward; they usually come from memories that you have not fully processed.

There are certain foods that can instantly connect me with my childhood. Most of us have things we loved to eat as children or have good memories about the preparation of food and celebrations where food was the main attraction. Memories that still warm my heart are the baking I did with my mother, making french fries from scratch with Grandma Bea and simply sitting in the kitchen with Grandma Connie who had huge wooden salad-serving utensils on her kitchen walls. Many events, brunches and potlucks remind me of friends and family.

3. Find 10 to 20 minutes once a day (or a few times if you can) to relax, close your eyes and breathe.

This is definitely one of the most challenging shifts that I have made and am still working on daily. If you are someone who is constantly on the go, you must make time to slow down, rest, relax and simply do nothing. This will allow you to be able to make more of every move that you do make, and the actions you take will be more mindful.

When I was growing up, dinnertime was a time to slow down and find out about each other's day. As I got older, I practiced the same ritual with my friends, roommates, boyfriend and extended family. Today, however, most people—including me—do not really stop and sit down for dinner, relax or even take those moments to breathe. I make things in mostly one pot or bowl—a lot of veggies or salad and some kind of protein—but usually do not set a table or use the proper utensils. I might stop at a store and buy prepared food, order delivery to my door or go out to a restaurant with friends or by myself. I know that I need to eat, but after a long day the thought of preparing and cleaning up after a meal seems overwhelming. It is easier to prepare food for others than for myself.

4. Clear your clutter by cleaning your space, and thus your mind, kitchen and body.

   This is one of the most important actions. You need to be free of excess to keep your mind, body and soul relaxed. Your surroundings tell a lot about you as a person; the cleaner and clearer your environment, the healthier your well-being and lifestyle.

   My mom is the master of "clean as you go." This is definitely something that I continue to do in my kitchen practices—to clean as I cook, bake or prep for a meal. You should keep your kitchen clear of clutter. When your cookies are baked, the salad is ready to be dressed and the meal placed on the table, you should not have to look in the kitchen and be stressed out by a mess. Make sure to have all of the ingredients for the recipe you are going to make. Try to put things away as soon as you have used them, and back where they belong so that you can find them the next time. Then simply relax and enjoy what you have made!

5. Observe when your mind is in the past or future and bring it back to the present.

   Have you ever seen anyone have a genuine love affair with food? It's an absolute joy to watch people fully immerse themselves in the flavors of a dish. Take one sensory experience and allow it to stop time. Enjoy a meal, savor an essential oil, spend time with a painting or watching a sunset, listen to enchanting music—these kinds of activities will not only bring you into the present moment but they can even create spiritual experiences. The practice of creating focus can increase your present-moment awareness.

6. Connect with nature: Sit on some grass or a rock, lean on a tree, listen to the ocean or do anything that makes you feel connected to the natural world. When you take time to be outside—from the woods to the sea—you can become more aware of the earth's power to help you feel grounded and alive.

Although I referred to connecting to nature mostly in the outdoors, you can do the same thing in your kitchen with fresh foods, spices and even utensils made from natural resources, like wooden spoons. Doing this allows you to think about your connection to the larger world and how what you do and eat is connected to the environment. Where did those strawberries come from? What kind of wood are your chopping boards and salad bowls made of? How were those cinnamon sticks gathered and dried, and what are you going to use them for?

7. Your body must be happy and that means eating regularly and well. Eat when you are hungry and choose what you eat with purpose. Take your time eating and make a connection to your food. Enjoy each meal and the time that you have with and around food—including when preparing a meal for someone else. All things made with *love* have power.

   Food is magical. It is so important to everyone, especially those who, like me, are mindful about the food they eat and how they prepare it. Figure out what foods you enjoy, make you happy, give you energy or even slow you down. What is a food that you like to prepare, cannot live without or are allergic to? Paying close attention to how what you eat makes you feel will help you to avoid problem foods and indulge in the ones you love.

Something for You to Try

Here's something that you can practice alone or with family and friends: Each time you eat, try slowing down for a few mindful bites. You can then practice for a whole meal, a full day, a week and eventually all of the time. Mindfulness helps us to become more aware of our reactions to food and eating, as well as our habits around mealtime. Did you do it alone? With a friend? A small group? What did you observe? How long did a particular habit last—a few bites? A meal? A week?

The following activities can help you integrate mindfulness into your life:

1. *Immerse yourself in the moment:* We are often distracted—by our phones, other people, our thoughts. The next time that you are performing a simple duty like brushing your teeth, make a commitment to be all there. Put away your phone,

turn off your TV or music, and truly appreciate being fully present. Pay attention to every detail of every activity in which you engage. This allows you to explore new experiences and sensations while performing what could otherwise be a menial, mindless task. Focusing your mind on every action cultivates mindfulness and the first place to start is with everyday, ordinary acts. Treat chores like washing dishes as mindfulness experiments and you may come to enjoy such tasks!

2. *Create something:* Creative thinking is a great way to work toward mindfulness and is a form of meditation. When undertaking challenging and creative work, your mind is completely focused and you enter a state of heightened awareness and consciousness. You are channeling your energy in a positive and constructive manner. This allows your mind to become doubly aware as it works creatively on the project at hand.

    Your creation doesn't need to be a masterpiece. It can be as simple as doodling on a piece of paper, or baking or singing along with a favorite song. The key is using the moment to invest your mental and physical energy in something that forces you to focus and flex your creative muscles. Creativity and self-expression also teach you to put faith in what you're doing. This can help you to better understand yourself, an important pillar of mindfulness.

3. *Yoga:* If sitting quietly isn't your style, then yoga may be the answer. Yoga takes the benefits of meditation and expresses them through the body. In addition to helping you become more in tune with yourself, yoga strengthens the connection between mind and body. It can be hard to motivate yourself to leave the house or may be inconvenient to go to a yoga class, but it's easy to practice yoga at home. YouTube has a great collection of yoga classes for complete beginners as well as expert yogis. Practicing yoga and achieving greater mindfulness can be just as easy as clicking on a video.

4. *Meditation:* It sounds simple to some and for many it's scary. Taking up the practice of meditation can seem intimidating as it's something that many people dedicate their whole lives to perfecting. However, meditation can be integrated into even the busiest person's life. It has so many benefits and can help

to mentally balance, focus and relax you. While meditation is an ancient art, it doesn't need to be complicated or confusing. Apps like Brain Wave, with 32 binaural programs, make meditation pretty easy.

Meditation is all about achieving mindfulness of your body and surroundings while acknowledging and coming to peace with them: the good, the bad and the ugly that you might see, think about and feel. By meditating, you can become a lot more connected with yourself and the world around you, and can carry this lesson of mindfulness to other aspects of your life. Meditation will help to put you on the path to mindfulness in your everyday life and will eventually become the center of your lifestyle as you become more mindful of its benefits.

MINDFUL MENU

Bacon Chicken Burgers with BBQ Sauce

♥

Baked Green Bean Sticks

Blessing

(A Mennonite Grace)

Thank you for the wind and the rain
And sun and pleasant weather.
Thank you for this our food
And that we are together. Amen.

Bacon Chicken Burgers | YIELDS 4 BURGERS

INGREDIENTS

3 slices turkey bacon

1 lb boneless, skinless and trimmed chicken breast

1 large egg, lightly beaten

½ tsp dried onion

¼ tsp garlic powder

¼ tsp freshly ground black pepper (or to taste)

½ tsp coarse sea salt

4 low-calorie white or wheat hamburger buns, lightly toasted

¼ cup BBQ sauce

½ cup shredded romaine lettuce

1–2 tomatoes, sliced

DIRECTIONS

1. Lightly coat a large pan with nonstick cooking spray, and briefly preheat over medium-low heat. Lay the bacon in the pan, making sure the slices don't overlap. Cook for about 3–5 minutes,

or until crispy, making sure to flip the bacon once every 30–60 seconds to prevent burning. Lay the cooked bacon onto a paper-towel-lined plate, and wipe off any remaining grease with another paper towel. Once cool, chop or crumble the bacon.

2. Chop the chicken into small chunks, and add to a food processor. Whiz until finely chopped. Add the ground chicken to a large bowl, along with the crumbled bacon, egg, dried onion, garlic powder and pepper. Gently mix with your hands until everything is evenly distributed throughout. (Optional: Cover and chill the bowl for at least 30 minutes to allow the flavors to marry.)

3. Lightly coat a clean large pan with nonstick cooking spray, and briefly preheat over medium-low heat. Shape the chicken mixture into 4 patties, and lightly sprinkle each side with the sea salt. Place in the pan, and cook for 3–4 minutes per side, or until no longer pink in the center. Once done, remove onto a plate to rest for 2 minutes.

4. To assemble, spread 1½ teaspoons of BBQ sauce onto each bun half. Place one burger patty onto each bottom bun, and top with lettuce and tomatoes. Place the other bun half on top.

Baked Green Bean Sticks | YIELDS 4–6 PORTIONS

INGREDIENTS

1 lb fresh green beans, washed and trimmed

3 tbsp olive oil

½ cup grated Parmesan cheese

1 tsp kosher salt

1 tsp freshly ground pepper

½ tsp paprika

DIRECTIONS

1. Preheat the oven to 375°F. Line a baking sheet with parchment paper.

2. In a large bowl, toss the green beans with the olive oil. Add the Parmesan, salt, pepper and paprika and toss well to coat.

3. Pour the green beans onto the baking sheet and bake until crisp, 10 to 15 minutes. Cool slightly before serving.

THE YOGA OF EATING
by Chris Block

Eating defines a primal relationship between self and world, the receiving of sustenance and nurture. It is the tangible embodiment of the elemental relations of giving and taking. Through these relations, we can answer the questions "How do I choose to be in the world?" and "How do I choose to be?"

—*The Yoga of Eating* by Charles Eisenstein

When working with a group of young leaders and engineers at a Silicon Valley technology company around mindfulness and relationship building, it was clear by noon that the participants weren't buying what I was selling, and I was going down in flames. After lunch I showed the "Where's the Gorilla?" video from YouTube. It's a great way to test awareness of our environment and the obvious things that we often miss. In the video, a number of people pass a basketball from one to another and count how many passes occur. It takes a fair amount of concentration and, in the middle of the exercise, a gorilla steps in, pounds his chest and then exits. Remarkably, a significant number of people don't see the gorilla! Our minds are conditioned to focus on the matter at hand, in this case counting the number of times a basketball is passed, and our concentration cannot be interrupted, even by the random appearance of a 600-pound gorilla. When the video is played a second time, viewers can't believe they missed it.

How many things do we miss in our lives because we are too busy to notice? It is when we slow down and pay attention, perhaps by sitting quietly and focusing on our breathing, or eating slowly and consciously, that we are able to see and hear what we've been missing—even when it is painfully obvious!

After the video, I conducted a mindful-eating exercise in which the engineers spent two minutes eating something that they brought into the circle: a piece of fruit or some other snack, coffee or water. After consciously paying attention with all of their senses, I asked people to pair up and talk about the experience. This was followed by a large group discussion.

One of the participants had a Diet Coke and told the group that he drank a lot of it and had for a long time. He was clearly uncomfortable as he told the group that after many years of drinking this beverage, he didn't think that he liked it anymore and wasn't sure that he ever had. This was a revelation for him and he wondered what other things in his life no longer worked. Another participant made the same observation about the coffee he drank throughout the day. These observations led to a great discussion about the harm that a lack of awareness can cause, whether from eating food that is no longer enjoyed, staying in relationships that are no longer healthy or working on projects that can't succeed.

Mindful eating can be a powerful portal into the awareness of our interior condition, an ongoing practice that can have a profound impact on our lives and communities. There are several methods of meditation and conscious breathing that help you to achieve mindfulness in your daily life. A meditation practice can take just 10 minutes and will have a positive impact on your day if you do it first thing in the morning.

Practice sitting either on the floor or in a chair for five or 10 minutes with a timer in the following way:

- ♥ feet firmly planted on the ground
- ♥ back straight
- ♥ head sitting comfortably on the neck
- ♥ hands placed on each leg or clasped together
- ♥ eyes closed or open and looking a bit downward
- ♥ air entering the nostrils and going all the way down to the belly, then back up again and out of the mouth
- ♥ fully and comfortably breathing with awareness of each breath

We do this practice to:

- ♥ get in touch with our breath
- ♥ be aware of our bodies
- ♥ appreciate our environment
- ♥ truly listen

This exercise, which centers on the breath, is the foundation of a mindfulness practice. We breathe constantly and always in the present moment—we don't use past breaths to make up for a current lack of breathing, or plan to breathe in the future so that we don't have to breathe in the present. If I am going to have a busy day, I don't breathe more between 7 and 8 a.m. because I won't have time to breathe later, such as when I might eat a big breakfast because I won't have time for lunch. The good thing about breathing is that it always occurs in the moment, so an awareness of our breath necessarily brings us into the present.

As a result of my ongoing practice, I can now take a deep breath and get into the present moment in a way that was not before possible. I become acutely aware of the world around me—what are people really saying, what is critically essential to this community at this time, and how can I play a compassionate and active role right now in the transformation that we are trying to achieve in our beloved community?

Mindful eating is based on the principles of meditation. I ask people to get into a mindfulness posture and we do some deep breathing together. Each person then eats something familiar as mindfully as possible. I ask them to look at the water and the glass that holds it and really see it, appreciate the work that went into making the glass and the rain that made the water possible, observe how it is contained within the glass, feel its temperature against your hand, gently bring it to your mouth, take a small sip, feel the water on the tongue and roof of your mouth, slowly swallow, feel it travel all the way down to your stomach, and finish by breathing deeply and completely.

Mindfulness means maintaining a moment-by-moment awareness of our thoughts, feelings, bodily sensations and surrounding environment. It also involves acceptance. We pay attention to our thoughts and feelings without judging them, without believing that there's a right or wrong way to think or feel in any given moment. When we practice mindfulness, our thoughts tune into what we're sensing in the present moment rather than rehashing the past or imagining the future[2].

There are many tools and practices to help make us much more attuned to our interior condition and improve upon it. For example, yoga, sitting meditation and mindfulness practices can all be of great assistance in helping us to understand the ways in which we are dis-

---

2   www.greatergood.berkeley.edu/topic/mindfulness/definition#what_is

connected. And while a meditation practice can be many things, it must be done habitually and provide an opportunity to experience the four attributes of mindfulness listed above. We should consistently employ these tools to establish a mindful practice in our lives and therefore be able to call upon it when mattering the most.

When I teach people to learn mindfulness and increase awareness, I typically use the following three-step process.

Step 1: Ask yourself three essential questions:

1. Are you aware of yourself?
2. Are you aware of the effect that you have on others?
3. Are you aware of the effect that others have on you?

Step 2: Learn basic mindfulness techniques:

There are many tools that help people practice mindfulness, ranging from mindful breathing to eating and walking. These practices make you much more attuned to the state of your interior condition and, with steady practice, will greatly increase their overall effectiveness.

Step 3: Large-group commitment dialogue:

I ask people to do several mindfulness exercises with me, perhaps a simple breathing exercise or mindful eating and a walking meditation. I then ask them to write down their own daily mindfulness practice. Next, I ask people to pair up and discuss their practice with each other. The entire group then comes together for dialogue to answer these questions: What is your specific commitment to a regular practice? What are you doing every day to keep your interior in tip-top condition?

This integration of mindfulness into our lives is essential. In the same way that we shouldn't start an exercise regimen when we are on the verge of a heart attack, or begin saving for retirement when we turn 65, we shouldn't begin a mindfulness practice when we are in the midst of a crisis.

When we are born or start a family or begin a career, we often see things with a great deal of freshness and clarity, much like the view from a well-polished window. The vicissitudes of life can act like the passage of time on a window, causing it to become increasingly clouded or stained. We begin to use only a small portion of the window, a corner that is cleaner than the rest; as a result, our view is extremely restricted.

We typically go about our day-to-day business, being pulled into meetings, parking ourselves and then moving on. This makes a certain amount of sense in interactions at the superficial level that involve sharing information, exchanging pleasantries and maintaining the status quo—all of which are necessary activities in our daily lives.

The engineers with whom I worked in Silicon Valley, like the rest of us, spend the vast majority of their lives completing assignments. This is a necessary practice in our work and personal lives. But what about those times when we want to make a profound difference, when it is necessary, as author Peter Block puts it, "to create a future distinct from the past"?

To live mindfully is to acknowledge that there is always something operating at a much deeper level, which is from where innovation springs and creativity is waiting to emerge, even when we try ignore it. It is here that fundamental reality exists and where profound change manifests. It is also where authentic relationships are discovered and nurtured. A mindfulness practice regularly polishes the window and, as a result, our life's view is much clearer and broader, which is why beginning a difficult process demanding deep collaboration over a long period of time is greatly enhanced by sharing a mindful meal together.

Set up the room to assure that people are comfortable and can easily talk to one another—large round tables are often best. Begin with grace or a blessing that does not necessarily have to be religious; it can be as simple as reminding people that they have gathered together to be part of something larger than themselves and that the community is depending on them to act wisely. This should be followed by a brief period of silence and a reminder for everyone to breathe deeply into that silence, which creates awareness of the interrelationships between us. Dessert is a good time to bring people back to the "center" and ask them to share their passion for the community and the reasons why they do their work.

A mindfulness practice is a way to keep polishing the window of our lives, allowing us to actually see the possibilities that exist to live life fully, experience our families completely and have fulfilling careers.

MINDFUL MENU

One-Pot Sausage and Veggies

BLESSING

(from the Unitarian tradition)

The bread we share this day is sacred.
The drink we share this day is sacred.
The friendship we share this day is sacred.
The laughter we share this day is sacred.
The stillness we share this day is sacred.
For bread, for friends, for joy and sorrow, for the comfort
of quietness:
Let us ever be grateful and caring.

One-Pot Sausage and Veggies | YIELDS 8 PORTIONS

INGREDIENTS

2 cups baby potatoes, rinsed and quartered

½ red bell pepper, sliced

½ yellow bell pepper, sliced

½ green bell pepper, sliced

1 zucchini, halved and sliced

½ onion, sliced

9 oz smoked sausage, sliced (not ground sausage)

3 tbsp olive oil

¼ tsp red pepper flakes (optional)

½ tsp garlic powder or minced garlic

1 tbsp Italian seasoning

½ cup low-sodium chicken broth

salt and fresh cracked pepper

fresh parsley, chopped

DIRECTIONS

1. In a heavy-bottomed pot, heat 2 tablespoons olive oil over medium-high heat. Add the baby potatoes to the pot and season with salt and pepper. Fry until golden brown and cooked through, around 8–10 minutes, stirring a few times. Remove potatoes from the pot and set aside.

2. In the same pot, brown the sliced sausage for around 5 minutes in 1 tablespoon of olive oil over medium-high heat. Remove the sausage from the pot and set aside.

3. Add onion and garlic and cook for 1 to 2 minutes with remaining cooking oil. Add the bell peppers and zucchini to the same pot and season with red pepper flakes, Italian seasoning, salt and pepper. Cook for 2 minutes until softened, stirring occasionally.

4. Add the cooked sausage and potatoes back to the pot and mix everything together. Add chicken broth and cook for 5 minutes more. Adjust seasoning and garnish with chopped fresh parsley. Serve immediately.

THE AGE OF AWARENESS IN THE GARDEN
by Claude E. Nunn III

Then God said, "I give you every seed-bearing plant on the face of the whole earth and every tree that has fruit with seed in it. They will be yours for food."

—Genesis 1:29 (NIV)

Cultivating a lifestyle of health, wellness and nutrition—"3n1"—is certainly the best power move to take full control of our bodies, minds and spirit; the sum of all these parts is greater than any one. Daily learning and searching for unbiased and truthful golden nuggets of mindful and conscious awareness is essential in our personal journeys. After my mother became ill with heart disease, I began a journey to understand the way food affects health—to take the lessons learned and apply them to my own life and the lives of my family and friends. I want to begin by telling the story of my parents and grandparents. I think it illustrates how we transitioned from eating "off the land" in ways that were healthy and sustainable to a more mechanized, unbalanced and unhealthy diet.

My mother was raised in Arkansas with 12 brothers and sisters. Grandpa and Grandma were sharecroppers. They worked on the owner's land for squatting rights. The house where they lived had a dirt floor, no running water inside, an outhouse and a firepit in kitchen as the main source of heat.

When I was growing up in California, my three brothers and I eagerly looked forward to the family history Mother shared with us every Sunday after dinner. She told us stories about how she grew up and also shared the family history that had been passed down to her. I realized the hardship that she and my aunts and uncles endured as children. They were always pressed to work hard during spring and summer to have enough to feed all those mouths during the cold winter months. My mother instilled the value of everyone doing their part and always working hard. She was third from the oldest, and the one leaned on the most to lead the others.

Before she was old enough to work out in the fields picking cotton or tobacco, my mother had to clean the house, do laundry, babysit and prepare dinner for the family. There was no refrigerator, no washer and dryer, no range and oven, no ironing board and no running water. My mother was not looking for sympathy when she told us her stories. Rather, she was making sure that we—her sons—knew where we came from.

Sundays were the Lord's Day, Sunday school, church service and Sunday dinner. My mother's family rarely ate meat except for Sunday dinner and it was usually fish that someone had caught or small game that someone had hunted or trapped. They had a garden that was seeded, tilled and harvested by hand; it provided food for so many hungry mouths. The vegetables that were grown in the garden made up all the meals for all those mouths.

My mother moved to California when she was 19 years old after graduating from college in Humphrey, Alabama. Mother was 22 years old when I was born, the first of her four sons. She raised us for the most part; Dad wasn't around after I turned about 7 or 8 years. The lessons she learned as a child served her well as she raised her own family. Besides taking care of the household and all that it entailed, she also managed an electronics school and another full-time job. As most parents do, my mother wanted her children to have a better life than she did. Because she didn't have meat on the table growing up, she made sure that we had meat every day, that her children had more than she did when she was a child.

I wanted to tell the story of my mother and her upbringing that relied on hard work, frugality and wholesome food. But those healthy habits were replaced by others when she found herself able to afford daily meat and processed foods.

At age 69 my mother had a stroke and the doctors saved her life after doing bypass surgery. We were terrified that we would lose her. I asked the doctors what had caused the stroke. And exactly what is a bypass? The doctor told us that they had to open her chest with small incisions to hone out the plaque and insert stents in the arteries that needed reinforcement. I imagined the pain and suffering my mother must have experienced and I was mad. Mad at not knowing why.

I asked the doctor what plaque was and where it came from. He gave me an education lesson that changed my life, my attitude towards food and how it affects our health. The doctor told me that plaque is saturated fat that is only present in animal products.

Mother Nature's Raw Foods vs. Dead Foods

Cooked foods are those void of nutrition because heat kills and destroys the delicate vitamins, antioxidants, probiotics and other essentials. So the best cooking method for vegetables is not stewing them for long periods of time but quickly sautéing or blanching to save the precious nutrients our bodies need. A completely raw diet or vegetarian/vegan diet is neither realistic nor very appealing to most. If you must eat meat, make sure it is free-range and wild-caught. Factory-produced farm animals of all kinds have high levels of bacteria, antibiotics, hormones, steroids and many other contaminants that you don't want in your food. Remember that processed foods are dead foods, which take up space and energy the body needs to rejuvenate and help reverse damages of which you are not yet even aware.

Powerball Foods: Foods That Kill and Super Foods That Heal

We all know the dangers of eating processed foods. But it doesn't seem to stop us from putting those foods in our mouths. Why is this so complicated for people? We need to know what we are up against in this battle that we are forced to fight daily. Big business is advertising their products constantly on television, the Internet, phones, magazines, radio—we can't get away from it, ever! These ads are developed and targeted to control and influence who we are, what we are, how we live our lives and what we eat. According to the food-as-medicine organization, Forks Over Knives, following the Standard American Diet (S.A.D.) puts us on a one-way collision with disease. We cannot consume sodas, burgers, pizza, sugary, salty, fatty foods every day and not be affected by this epidemic.

Twenty-five percent of America's calories come from animal-based foods and 12% from plant-based foods. Only 6% of America's calories are coming from healthy fruits, vegetables, whole grains, nuts and seeds.[3] Heart disease, type 2 diabetes, obesity, cancer, inflammation and a myriad of other diseases and their complications affect all age groups including our young children. The diseases

---

3   https://www.forksoverknives.com/standard-american-diet-sadder-than-we-thought/.

caused by an unnatural diet are so rampant that they are now accepted as an inevitable part of aging. When I talk critically about diet, people often give the excuse that they want to eat food that tastes good, or they don't have time or that healthy food is expensive. I say those excuses are just that: excuses. I can tell you that anyone can make a vegetarian meal taste better than a typical meat-based meal without the collateral health damage and for less money and little preparation time.

I am a classically trained chef and have been cooking for more than 30 years. I can say with certainty that saturated fat, salt and sugar are the main ingredients that make food taste a certain way that our brain receptors yearn for; indulging those yearnings is not a good thing. Most of the processed foods, convenience foods, junk foods, packaged foods, frozen foods and GMO (genetically modified organism) foods, and those with high concentrations of nitrates, antibiotics, hormones and chemicals become toxins in our bodies. They do more harm than good, if they do any good at all; I call these low-octane foods. Medical doctors, researchers and scientists all conclude that our bodies cannot keep up with this daily onslaught of toxins. We need to detox and supplement with raw foods, juicing, sprouting, superfoods, whole grains, fermented foods, nuts and seeds. We can reverse our unhealthy lifestyles and walk a straighter line to health and wellness. When we replace low-octane foods with high-octane foods, our bodies will repair, renew, replenish, recharge and regenerate on a cellular level, bringing to life the complex synergy of "3n1" vibrational energies. High-octane superfoods are organic, wild-crafted, homegrown, community-gardened or purchased from co-ops and farmer's markets.

Many people ask me to condense my teaching about food and wellness to a simple list of recommendations that can be easily followed. My advice is to be as mindful as you can about the food choices you make. Stop, just for a few moments, before you pull into the fast-food drive thru or reach into the freezer at the supermarket for a processed frozen dinner. It takes time to cultivate healthy eating, but when you do, you will also experience a shift in every aspect of your life—the spiritual, emotional and physical. My recommendations for developing a truly healthy lifestyle are listed below:

♥ Eat a simple diet of ancient grains, sprouted beans, nuts and organic vegetables.

♥ Grow some of your own foods, even if it's only a few things in pots on the porch.

♥ Incorporate these herbs into your daily diet: garlic, turmeric and ginger.

♥ Indulge a little as a reward, such as meal-replacement bars, pro bars and vegan greens

♥ Expand knowledge in foraging edibles, mushrooms, roots, herbs and seaweeds.

♥ Use and make elixirs, tinctures, oils and ointments.

♥ Use organic/wild-crafted supplements such as Green Vibrance and Rockin' Wellness.

♥ Exercise—yoga, swimming, hiking, gym, martial arts, cycling or running.

MINDFUL MENU

Madagascar Red Rice ♥ Stir-Fry Vegetables

BLESSING
(Christian Grace)

Heavenly Father,
We thank you for all things small and great.
Please bless this food for the nourishment, wisdom and
enlightenment of our body, soul and spirit. We give you
praise, honor and glory.
In Jesus' name, amen.

Madagascar Red Rice or
Forbidden Black Rice with Stir-Fry Vegetables | YIELDS 6 PORTIONS

INGREDIENTS

½ cup red or black rice

1½ cup vegetable stock

1 bay leaf

2 garlic cloves (minced)

½ cup white onion (diced)

2 tbsp ginger root (chopped fine)

½ cup wild mushrooms (sliced)

¼ cup hot or sweet fresh peppers (diced)

¼ cup carrots (diced)

¼ cup yellow squash (diced)

¼ cup green beans (diced)

¼ cup broccoli (chopped)

½ cup bok choy or leafy greens

salt and pepper to taste

DIRECTIONS

1. In saucepan add washed rice and sauté (1 tablespoon oil) for 5 minutes, then add vegetable stock, bay leaf and 2-inch lemongrass stalk, cook for 20 minutes. Set aside covered.

2. Slice, dice and julienne vegetables. Blanch the broccoli, beans and carrots for 2 minutes, chill in cold water. Do not overcook.

3. In a hot sauté pan or wok, add 2 tablespoons grapeseed oil, onions, garlic and ginger sauté until translucent, add squash and mushrooms and cook 2 minutes, add peppers and blanched vegetables. Sauté 2 more minutes, add salt, pepper and herbs to taste.

4. Put the rice first in a bowl and add vegetables on top. Finish with soy sauce or Braggs Amino.

SOCIOECONOMIC EATING
by Adam J. Joseph

As far back as I can remember, I ate well. Everything that I was taught was all about what was good for me. Spirituality, culture, food and tradition were such a huge part of my family's existence. My grandmother (Enid Willis) was born and raised in Jamaica, and my grandfather (Jackson Willis) was from Evansville, IN. They met in England during the blitz of World War II; cultures and mindfulness were to be united, cultivated and continued stateside as they laid their foundation for what we have practiced to this day. For many families much like ours, mindful eating was a way of life. Along with utilizing the resources that were available came a hard work ethic and physical activity.

Mindful eating, thinking, being and sustainability weren't trends but ways of life. My grandparents were hard-working folks who refused to accept welfare for too long but were grateful to have it when needed. They used their resources to the best of their ability, stretching food as far as they could and teaching their kids to do the same. As children of the Great Depression, living frugally wasn't new to my grandparents; it was just how things had always been and continued to be. Powdered eggs, milk and "government cheese" were made into delicacies using imagination and creativity. My mother and her brothers and sisters had to augment and tinker with recipes to make their ingredients comparable to what the recipes actually called for. No recipes call for "2 cups of powdered milk" or "4 powdered eggs," so trial and error played a big part in mastering meal preparation. In addition to the minimal government assistance that my grandparents accepted, they gardened, maintained an apple tree and traded commodities with other families who were in the same boat. Vegetables, apples and whatever else they acquired were frozen for the winter and spring.

I was told that my grandparents had to provide for six children. In the midst of racial inequalities, they were forced to take jobs that required my grandfather to work in St. Louis during the week at Chrysler, and my grandmother to work late hours at a hospital—decent jobs for hard workers. These circumstances required thoughtful planning for meals, as they didn't earn substantial wages and far from enough for everyone to eat "high off the hog." There was no fast food nor frivolous snacks and nothing was wasted. Everyone went to church, had chores inside and out, walked to school and played hard. After a day like that nobody was going to pass up a meal. Everyone stayed in good physical shape. They weren't overweight and managed to avoid health issues related to poor nutrition. As early as 8 years old, I witnessed the truths of my mother's stories about the importance of eating and living right every time I looked in the mirror or at my grandparents, their children and, later, my cousins. I often wondered how my grandparents did it, being black and raising six kids during the '40s, '50s and '60s given the conditions, and providing good meals that were nutritious, delicious and balanced.

What Did Our Forefathers Eat?

In an intriguing article, Joseph E. Holloway, Ph.D. (California State University, Northridge) explains in detail many of the crops brought to the United States by slaves from Africa:

> *Without question, yams were the most common African staple fed to enslaved Africans on board ships bound for the Americas. The slave merchant John Barbot, for example, noted that "a ship that takes in 500 slaves, must provide above 100,000 yams," or roughly 200 per person. The ship logs of the slave vessel Elizabeth, bound for Rhode Island in 1754, listed provisions of "yams, plantain, bread [cornbread], fish and rice." In another example, the account books of the slave ship Othello (1768–69) listed hundreds of baskets of yams taken on board as provisions along with lesser quantities of plantains, limes, pepper, palm oil, and gobba-gobs (goobers, or peanuts).[4]*

Dr. Holloway says that additional foods such as black-eyed peas and peanuts (which are actually legumes), sesame seeds and okra were brought from Africa. These items were nutritious especially when paired with other complex carbohydrates, proteins and vegetables. This diet is obviously contrary to the one slave masters inflicted on displaced Africans. The American slave diet consisted of an abundance of fatty pork "parts," much of which was cured because of lack of refrigeration. It was from these conditions and resourceful-

---

4   http://worldartswest.org

ness that songs like "Hambone" came about—African slaves having to make do and support one another through rough times.

In addition, slaves were given molasses because it was believed to be good for them and were discouraged from eating fruits, as they were thought to make them sick. Many of the slaves were lactose intolerant because dairy was not a major part of their cultural diet, consumed instead by the slaves' masters and many slave children.

What Do We Eat Now?

Many households today are headed by single parents who face the demands of work and childcare. Providing nutritious meals can seem an impossible task. Having been a single father of three children, even with a family background that emphasized the value of cooking and eating good food, it is hard to make sure that everyone (including me) eats well. Fortunately, because of great genetics, many of my shortcomings as a parent haven't affected me or my children negatively. They go to schools that provide well-balanced lunches and have been taught what snacks to eat and when.

In many households today, children are often at home alone for a few hours each day. Moms and dads work late or have second jobs, and may not have time to prepare a meal every night. This is something that I can attest to firsthand. My wife and I had to live in separate households for a period of time and found ourselves having to plan nutritious meals in advance, while including leftovers in our weekly plans as well. In addition, considering our schedules and financial resources, we have to monitor the kinds of snacks that our children can have at home and school. My wife and I both work and, with kids in track, football, wrestling, baseball and other extracurricular activities, we have to make sure that we spend our money on food that supports all of our lifestyles, while providing energy and nourishment.

Fortunately, both my wife and I grew up in households where we saw healthy food prepared and served at every meal, every day. Growing up, we did not have chips, pop and a lot of candy in the house. Our parents gave us apples, oranges, bananas, nuts and other snacks that were not filled with empty calories or high levels of sodium. Providing these types of meals and snacks today takes some thought but becomes easier day by day, and creates a mindful-eating legacy for generations to come.

As a recipient of Supplemental Nutritional Assistance Program (SNAP) benefits, I made sure that I used those extra dollars to get the biggest nutritional bang for the buck. We often see other recipients filling their grocery baskets with chips, pop, ice cream, a lot of whole and processed meats, frozen foods and processed snacks. With what we are seeing in the grocery baskets, and looking at ourselves and our children, it seems as though many are unaware that the 'N' in SNAP stands for "Nutritional." In 2014 the SNAP program provided $74.1 billion to roughly 46.5 million Americans. Unfortunately, many of those dollars were spent by families buying food items that weren't nutritionally beneficial to them or their children.

> *SNAP-Ed, formerly known as the Family Nutrition Program and Food Stamp Nutrition Education, began in 1988 when cooperative extension faculty in Brown County, Wisconsin, and University of Wisconsin extension staff discovered that by committing state and local funding and contracting with the state SNAP agency, an equal amount of federal dollars could be secured to expand the reach of nutrition education to low-income persons in that area. Other universities soon followed. In 1992, seven states conducted SNAP-Ed using $661,000 in federal funds. By 2004, SNAP-Ed was conducted throughout the country using nearly $460 million, with $228.6 million in SNAP administration funds and the remainder contributed by the states.[5]*

Not only are there additional funds and resources for the SNAP-Ed program, which is growing every year, but there are also many partners participating in the program. Farmers are working with state and local communities to provide fresh fruits and vegetables to SNAP recipients; all-natural stores that provide healthy snacks, fruits and vegetables are accepting these benefits as well. In addition, some markets may provide in-store cooking demonstrations and recipes for healthy, mindful eating. So what part of the socioeconomic-status problem is prohibiting these recipients from taking advantage of such resources? Could it be where they live and not having a way to access farmers' markets and whole-foods markets? Many families receiving benefits don't have transportation; they walk to the nearest grocery store and wheel their bags home in grocery carts. Could it

---

5   https://nifa.usda.gov

be that prices of the whole and all-natural foods are unaffordable for low-income families? Many times shoppers are looking for the easy grab-and-go foods and either don't care about or believe what they hear about the danger of over-processed and some prepared foods. Brittany Chin, RN, LD, writes: *The proof lies in the pudding when it comes to foods that are good for your health.... I encourage my patients to focus on "whole foods" that are nutrient dense rather than "processed foods" that are energy dense.*[6] She also recommends gardening your own foods and finding a local CSA (Community Supported Agriculture).

My mother prided herself on how little she spent at the grocery store, because she supplemented our meals with foods from our garden. As we were fortunate enough to live in a home that had a front and back yard, we gardened almost year-round. This is where I got a majority of my physical activity growing up. The saying with mom was, "You don't work, you don't eat." She meant that literally and figuratively, as it pertained directly to me and to the many other families who came before us and learned to sustain themselves. My mother taught me at a very young age about cost control and the food she was buying, as well as how far she could stretch it and what the benefits were—paired with the physical activity I did—to "earn my keep." These are the things that, coupled with mindful thinking and eating, can help change a huge part of the socioeconomic issues that we are having today. I was taught by my single mother how to break down a whole chicken, because it was cheaper than buying it in parts. When we were done eating it, the carcass was placed in a pot with vegetables and complex carbohydrates and we made soup. What we didn't eat of the soup was then frozen.

Where Do We Go from Here?

1. Speak with local dietitians (or healthcare offices) about what foods are better to eat—and in what proportions—for you and your family. There are places that give free advice and screenings to let you know your current health and what steps to take to stay the same or get better! Be proactive rather than reactive. Whether you are a SNAP-benefit recipient or not, locate your local farmer's market and look into the vast variety of foods offered. This will vary from state to state, region to

---

6   http://www.foodandnutrition.org

region and season to season, but the health benefits will be well worth it for you and your family.

2. Research seasonal/sustainable foods based on what region you live in. Having relocated to Georgia in 2014, I've found that many hearty leafy greens can now be maintained and harvested year-round. If you aren't able to garden at home because of space and/or resources, there is also the option of community gardens (community-supported agriculture—CSAs). Prior to my mother and I living in a house, we occupied space in a community garden in Champaign, IL, that I believe is still there. In addition to that, you should research the proper freezing and/or extended preservation of any and all foods with a local regulatory authority to ensure that you are preserving your foods safely and in the best manner.

3. Stay active! Walk with your partner, run with the kids or join a group of individuals wanting to get healthy; do it together! Activity has been on top of the food pyramid for some time now. Eating healthy by itself won't do it. Our children need to be and stay active. Having three children in multiple sports and activities, I know what this can cost, but what I've found is that there are usually scholarships available for families who find it hard to pay the fees associated with these extracurricular activities. If you don't ask, you'll never know.

4. Educate our young people about where we came from and what was eaten then. Even if it wasn't the best, explain the importance of it now and for other family members to come, as well as for society as a whole.

MINDFUL MENU

Pasta and Homemade Tomato Sauce ♥ Farm Green Salad

Blessing
(from the Native American Iroquois tradition)

We return thanks to the corn, and to her sisters,
The beans and squashes, which give us life.
We return thanks to the bushes and trees,
Which provide us with fruit.
We return thanks to the Great Spirit,
In whom is embodied all goodness,
And who directs all things for the good of his children.

Simple and Healthy Tomato Sauce | YIELDS 6 PORTIONS

INGREDIENTS

¼ cup olive oil

6 cloves garlic, smashed

4 lb ripe tomatoes, stem section removed and cut into small chunks

2 tsp salt

pepper

2 tbsp dried basil

1 tbsp dried thyme

1 tbsp dried dill

2 tsp cumin

¼ tsp red pepper flakes

DIRECTIONS

1. Heat oil in a large, wide skillet or saucepan over medium heat. Add garlic and cook until fragrant, about 2 to 3 minutes.

2. Add tomatoes, increase the heat to high, and season with salt and pepper. Add herbs and spices, and stir to combine.

3. When mixture comes to a boil, reduce heat to low and let simmer for 1 to 2 hours (the longer it cooks, the less chunky it will become), stirring occasionally.

4. Taste and season with additional salt and pepper, if necessary.

5. Serve over 4 ounces of whole-wheat pasta of choice.

Farm Green Salad | YIELDS 4 PORTIONS

INGREDIENTS

5 cups chopped romaine lettuce

1 small red onion, thinly sliced

1 cucumber, thinly sliced

½ cup cherry tomatoes, halved

¼ cup sliced Kalamata olives

¼ cup crumbled goat cheese

freshly ground black pepper, to taste

FOR THE LEMON VINAIGRETTE

¼ cup olive oil

¼ cup apple cider vinegar

zest of 1 lemon

3 tbsp freshly squeezed lemon juice

1½ tsp extra-fine granulated sugar (Imperial Sugar if possible)

DIRECTIONS

1. To make the vinaigrette, whisk together olive oil, apple cider vinegar, lemon zest, juice and sugar in a small bowl; set aside.

2. To assemble the salad, place romaine lettuce in a large bowl; top with red onion, cucumber, tomatoes, olives, goat cheese and pepper, to taste. Pour 2 tablespoons of dressing on top of each salad and gently toss to combine.

3. Serve immediately.

REGAINING OUR FOOD SOVEREIGNTY
by Njathi Kabui

As a food activist, I have learned that food plays a great role in health, wealth and identity. I cannot talk about food justice without touching on these three topics. To eat well, you often must have wealth; identity could be viewed as the nexus between wealth and health.

Wealth is a family and community endeavor. It's not just what a person acquires during a lifetime alone but what he or she inherits and then passes to the next generation. Wealth is also the story of how my family and clan utilized their time and opportunities, and what they passed on to me in the face of secondary factors such as oppression, exploitation and discrimination. Inheritance is not just material; skills and habits may also be inherited. The ability to work together, to be honest and frugal, influences the growth or decline of wealth to successive generations.

How well one manages inheritance is based on what one acquires along the way. There is a clear historical, economic and political context to the issues of wealth, health and identity. I am who I am due to the amount of wealth that my forebears accumulated; I am who I am due to the health and habits that were passed to me; and my identity is based on how much power that wealth and health has allowed me to possess relative to the society in which I live.

Mindful Eating in the Context of Power Balance

Michael Pollan, in his highly acclaimed *New York Times* article, "Unhappy Meals," made a serious attempt to understand why America continues to be dogged by the consequences of a bad diet. His conclusion was that the very people who are most influential in affecting what the American diet looks like also stand to gain the most when our health is broken. He concluded that the food industry, journalists and politicians are all responsible for the most part for the current state of the American plate.

This is a great place to start a conversation. Pollan explores the phenomenon of food as a product manufactured in factories and saturated with chemical nutrients and the ramifications for American consumers. His analysis speaks almost exclusively to the white American experience. Who can fault him for that? But the reality is that America is not all white, male and middle class. While Pollan does an admirable job articulating his position, marginalized voices need to contribute to the discussion of what is on the American plate.

America was built on the ruins of other cultures, including the Native Americans whose land was stolen through devious treaties and political subterfuge; the Africans who were brought to this country as slaves; other countries that were annexed as American territories; and the cheap labor of immigrants who continue to land on the shores of this country. I am sure that Pollan was not speaking on behalf of these people, for the truth is that their plate has rarely been happy. A person who is undocumented, occupied or enslaved cannot be expected to exercise the same mindfulness about food as the person who is occupying, enslaving or has the power to legalize his or her stay in this country.

We cannot solve the food and related health problems in America without first addressing the problematic foundation upon which this country was founded: Britain did not have the right to impose taxation without representation. Yet America was just as undemocratic as Britain in its treatment of African-American, female, landless and Native-American populations. The founders gave privilege to landholding white males. The preamble to the Constitution, "We the People," did not include all of those who lived and worked in the United States, and it still does not. How do you build a democratic country through undemocratic means? How do you bring about justice through unjust means?

America has always had a permanent underclass upon which its greatness was built, those who had the responsibility of undertaking the work that land-owning Americans did not want to do. Americans wanted to grow sugarcane and tobacco but did not want to pay for the labor. This created a dualism in this country—an upper class that wielded great power that was used to increase wealth and oppress those without resources of their own. And religion was also a tool of those in power. Religious teachings in this country, for the most part, sanctioned the ideas of the powerful and thus it developed the same dualism. That explains why there were segregated churches even though everyone was supposed to be praying to the same Deity.

Lies cannot endure forever and neither did the American one, as the dualism became an obvious contradiction to American values. Increased oppression eventually caused the oppressed to revolt against those in power; the attacks were not always directed toward those in power per se but to the *idea* of power in balance. It was the easiest target or argument for those seeking justice and, by pointing to the system's contradictions, they could thrust themselves into freedom just by pressuring those in power to harmonize those contradictions. This was the case, for example, with the civil-rights movement. Dr. Martin Luther King, Jr., quoted the preamble to the Declaration of Independence during the march on Washington, and he even went further to say that the "check that America had given to the Negro has been returned with the stamp of insufficient funds."

Present Conditions

It is crucial for the oppressed to understand that the dualism existing in America has resulted in the concentration of power within one group; those in power transfer an inordinate amount of resources to themselves. When oppression takes on gender, racial or religious lines, the power imbalance follows similar fault lines. For the group ceding resources, there are cultural, political, psychological, economic, linguistic and even spiritual consequences for such losses. Land that was previously available to the group may be lost, as has been the case for Native Americans and African Americans. Foodways may also be lost as displaced people become disorganized. Many of those with cultural knowledge may be displaced and even criminalized. Certain dances and ceremonies among Native Americans were criminalized during the American-Indian wars. Shamans and other community leaders were targeted among Native Americans and African Americans. In fact, the very possession of cultural knowledge that challenges the oppressor's logic is seen as a threat to power.

Logic has it that if the power imbalance has brought about the dehumanizing of one group by another, the oppressed have to engage in the business of humanizing. Like a prescription for a disease (oppression falls within this category), the cure has to be very specific in addressing the root causes of the disease, and address each and every tactic used by the oppressor.

Toward a Paradigm Shift

Those facing oppression must first start by understanding that there are different paradigms: those oppressed suffer twice, from poor foodways to the lack of food resources available to the larger society. For example, we can obtain healthy food at such stores as Whole Foods and farmers' markets but relatively few minorities can access those stores. This brings about the first order of business: deconstructing words in order to construct more appropriate theories and practices.

The term "food desert" has been used by many in communities of color and other oppressed groups to describe the lack of access to healthy food, with a very deliberate aim to avoid the problem's causes. The argument has been made that food insecurity is deliberately caused by governments, both federal and local, that make communities so poor that they cannot produce their own food. When you give such a phenomenon a neutral name and compare it to a natural desert, it obscures the hands of the authority that created the problem. The same is true when organic food is labeled as such and chemical-laden food is labeled as conventional. What is conventional about poisoning food? In a transparent society, manufacturers of chemical-laden food would have the burden of labeling their food, while chemical-free food would be just food. These are two examples that have very different implications to both the oppressed and larger society. The oppressed in this case cannot solve the problem by simply finding ways to bring food resources into their communities. They have to address the root cause of the problem as well as making culturally appropriate food available.

The second level of analysis would be to determine those areas where there is common ground. Heightened awareness is displayed by increased consumption of healthier foods, increased CSA (community-supported agriculture), increased number of farmers' markets and increased number of health-food stores across the country. This can offer grounds for a united front to make the healthy food movement multiracial, while helping to address both racial and health problems in this country.

The Way Forward

I have been having dinner around the country with the aim of addressing some of these issues. I came up with the name "Ecopological Eating," which means to connect food with the intention of addressing three basic issues: environment, politics and anthropology.

The root of the word economy is "eco," meaning home. Earth is home to all of us regardless of how much power we have and the dominant political system. We have to seriously ask ourselves how eating the way we do addresses inequities that have evolved over time. We are also a product of evolution and must take the long view of our health—who determines what we eat, how they acquired those powers and how that has affected how healthy we are. Only then can we really say that we are eating mindfully. Every bite and plate of food would be a vote for a more just and healthy food system that restores power for all. These practices would make America, for once, great and healthy; truly, wealth is what remains when your belly is full.

MINDFUL MENU

Ten-Minute Baked Tostada ♥ Quick Black Beans and Rice

BLESSING
(from Ghana)

Earth, when I am about to die
I lean on you.
Earth, while I am alive,
I depend on you.

Ten-Minute Oven-Baked Tostadas | YIELDS 6 PORTIONS

INGREDIENTS

6 corn tortillas

2 tbsp vegetable oil

pinch of salt

½ cup (total) of your favorite
tostada toppings (beans,

chicken, beef, lettuce,
cheese)

2–3 cups cooked, shredded
chicken

DIRECTIONS

1. Preheat the oven to 400°F.
2. Line a rimmed baking sheet with foil. Arrange as many tortillas as will fit on the baking sheet without overlapping.
3. Brush both sides of the tortillas lightly with oil and sprinkle with salt.
4. Bake for about 8 minutes, turning over after 4 minutes.

5. Remove from the oven and transfer to a paper-towel-lined tray to cool. It's OK if they're slightly soft as long as they're browned. They will crisp up even more as they cool.

6. Serve immediately with cooked chicken.

Quick and Easy Black Beans and Rice | YIELDS 6 PORTIONS

INGREDIENTS

2 tsp canola oil

1 small onion, peeled and chopped

1 clove garlic, peeled and chopped

1 tsp ground cumin

1 tsp ground chili powder

2 oz canned roasted green chile peppers (half a small can)

2 cups cooked white rice

¼ cup red sofrito (available in supermarkets, in the Latino foods section)

15-oz can black beans, rinsed and drained

¼ tsp kosher salt

¼ tsp black pepper

DIRECTIONS

1. In a large nonstick frying pan, heat the oil over medium-low heat. Add the onion and cook 2–3 minutes until soft and translucent. Stir in the garlic, cumin, chili powder and green chile peppers and cook for 2 minutes.

2. If the rice is cold, break it up with your hands as you add it to the pot. Stir well to combine the rice and onion mixture; cook, stirring, for 2–3 minutes until the rice is warmed through. Add in the sofrito and black beans, and stir gently until the sofrito is incorporated and the beans evenly distributed throughout the rice.

3. Season with the salt and pepper. Taste and add more if needed.

4. Serve warm, or cool completely and refrigerate.

(You can make this up to two days in advance; add a few drops of water and reheat in the microwave.)

BIGGER THAN ME:
MINDFULNESS AND COMMUNITY FOOD WORK
by Anzia Bennett

Taking Care of Ourselves

The practice of mindfulness offers a path to live life with a deeper sense of intentionality and awareness, a more thoughtful way of engaging with the world, and the tools to help be fully present in our lives and community. As community-engaged practitioners committed to social-justice work, we are too often overwhelmed by the weight of responsibilities at work and at home, the hopelessness that we feel facing the depths of racism, patriarchy, colonialism, oppression, social and structural inequities, and the very real needs of our communities.

Even as we celebrate successful organizing campaigns, legislative wins and the construction of new community gardens, and are amazed by the strength, insight and power of our communities, we often forget to take care of ourselves. Mindful practice offers a strategy to remember ourselves in our work. We need to be aware of what we know, are feeling and need so that we can feel sustained and find joy in our lives, and can keep on working.

But mindfulness is useful *in* our work as well. It is more than an individual-level practice—it provides a path to more effective community work that gives weight to the experience and knowledge present in our communities. It helps us slow down, create spaces to listen to each other, and acknowledge what we know, what we need and how best to get there.

Mindful eating is often articulated as a way for individuals to improve their own health, change behaviors related to food preparation and consumption, and become more aware of how their food choices impact the world around them. It is frequently proposed as a means of promoting weight loss. And while all of these are important outcomes, it is crucial to remember that mindfulness is also rooted in love for community, not *just* love for the individual. As community-engaged practitioners committed to improving the health and wellness of our beloved communities, we both celebrate and work to expand the concept of mindfulness as it relates to how we understand the role of food in our lives.

Mindful practice enables a deep interrogation of our food system and creates space to intentionally embrace and share what our communities know about growing and preparing the foods that sustain us. It allows us to define health broadly. This essay offers suggestions about ways that we can employ mindful eating in our community work—by introducing some key principles, questions and activities that can help build this process into our work. The key is to intentionally embrace what our communities already know about cultivating, cooking and eating healthy food, and sharing strategies to more consciously use food as medicine.

Expanding the Conversation

We know that food is a core part of our identities, and our attitude towards and relationship to food signals how we love ourselves and our communities. It is central to bringing people together and to nourishing our souls. So we work to have a more mindful relationship with food—to pay attention to what we put in our bodies, to listen to our bodies as we eat and to understand that food is medicine.

We work to apply these same principles as we cook with and for our communities, and we see shared cooking and eating as opportunities to build critical community consciousness about our current food system and its unhealthy impacts on our communities. As we think about mindful eating in the context of community work, we ask ourselves: How do we incorporate the components of mindfulness as we cook with and for our communities? How do we think about how the food we grow, purchase, prepare, serve and consume reflects our core values as people committed to creating healthier communities? How do we celebrate traditional food knowledge? How do we share strategies for healthier cooking and eating without making people feel ashamed or guilty about their cooking and eating habits? How do we identify and deconstruct the ways that food traditions and practices in communities of color and poor communities are often used to shame and blame people for negative health outcomes? How do we situate our food choices within the larger food system? What do we talk about as we eat together? How does the kitchen table create a safe space for community building, bridging, organizing, learning, solidarity and celebration?

Eating Real Food Together

Cultivating mindful eating practice at the community level starts with the simple act of eating real food together. We cook for weekly staff meetings so that those working at the grassroots level feel sustained for the work that simultaneously keeps them up at night and feeds their souls—so they know that someone took the time to cook with them in mind. We invite colleagues and community members into our kitchens to cook together and deepen our relationships. We bring homemade food to community meetings so that community members feel nourished and appreciated. We host community meals and potlucks. This simple act—of taking the time to prepare food for each other, and creating spaces for people to eat together—provides opportunities for people to feel loved and cared for. It helps combat feelings of isolation and fosters feelings of togetherness. Before we ask them to think about what they are eating so that they can begin to build awareness about what their bodies need, we are asking people simply to share a meal together, to feel the love of being cooked for, and to get to know their community around the table.

Eating What We Love

It is important that we are intentional in honoring the cooking traditions of our communities. We understand the definition of health to be broader than simple medical definitions of blood-sugar counts, pounds lost or gained, or BMI (body mass index). A healthy life means a life full of joy, of cultural pride, of feelings of togetherness and community, and of the very real satisfaction that comes from eating our favorite foods (regardless of their sodium content or calorie count). Healthy eating is more than just counting calories. It is feeling connected to something larger than ourselves. Eating dishes that may be deemed unhealthy is okay, sometimes, as long as we approach eating with the intention of finding balance.

Food brings us joy. It reminds us of home. It brings us comfort. And so as we plan menus for community events or when we lead community nutrition classes, we don't think about what we *shouldn't* eat. We think about the foods we want to celebrate. We think about where those foods come from. Who grew and harvested the ingredients? Where did the recipe come from? What strategies can we use to ensure that dishes provide the nutrients we need? How can we tailor traditional dishes for community members at risk or managing diabetes, heart disease and hypertension? We work to draw connections between the foods we love and the lives we want to live.

What we often find is that simply reflecting on dishes that our parents grew up eating—dishes that our grandparents cooked—helps us to remember healthier strategies for putting food on the table. Whether it is because our grandparents had to make do with less, cultivated their own garden plots or could walk to a market each day and purchase fresh produce, we often find that the dishes they put on the table illustrate the healthier approaches to eating that we are working to relearn. To be mindful and healthy when it comes to food does not require that we completely alter our diets. To be mindful simply means to be conscious about what we eat. We encourage each other to become aware of what our bodies want and need in order to understand the balance necessary to achieving a healthy diet.

More than Just Food
The next step in cultivating mindful eating practice at the community level is where it gets exciting. We have realized that applying the tenets of mindfulness actually helps expand the community work we do. It is more than helping to change individual eating behaviors and improve individual health. While the tenets of mindful eating offer an important approach to helping people reconnect with their bodies and improve their health, we hope to add to the conversation and show that mindfulness can be applied more broadly to community food work. We also believe that mindfulness work should include consciousness building around food justice. Helping people make connections between their individual food choices and behaviors, and the larger systems and structures that shape our relationships to food, are other expressions of mindfulness in action. While it is important to help people be present with their food choices, it is also important that they understand the context in which those choices are made. Food can serve as a powerful springboard for deep community education and organizing. Mindful eating practice provides a way to build consciousness about food justice and to develop critical analysis about the underlying causes of unhealthy eating.

So many of our cultural traditions and so much of our cultural pride centers on food. And yet so much of our relationship to food is clouded by feelings of guilt, shame, stress and obligation. We often shun the food traditions of our grandmothers for new food fads.

We forget that our families found ways to sustain themselves and get the nutrients they needed. In many ways, as our lives have gotten busier, more mechanized and moved further away from the land, we have become disconnected from the food practices that helped our ancestors stay nourished. This disconnection is no accident—it is tied directly to the powerful corporate food industry, historical land dispossession in communities of color and poor communities, the challenges of trying to survive in a struggling economy, the neoliberal turn in public health that blames health outcomes on personal responsibility, and other structural and systemic factors. While mindful eating practice is a powerful tool to help individuals make healthier choices about what and how they eat, we know that these individual choices are not happening in a vacuum. Rather, they offer a way to navigate the larger food system and societal relationships to food.

As community-engaged practitioners, it is important to think about the intentional and deliberate planning necessary to make change happen. When we teach our communities to understand food as medicine, how do we also celebrate the foods that bring us together, that nourish us? To address and do away with the guilt and shame that surrounds food for so many of us, we need to understand why our food system functions the way it does. Why do some communities seem to be plagued with certain nutrition-related chronic diseases while others are not? Why do certain neighborhoods have grocery stores that sell fresh, healthy food, while others do not? Why are foods full of sugar, fat and salt so cheap while fresh fruits and vegetables are often prohibitively expensive? Why is achieving optimal health harder than simply going on a diet or making healthier food choices? How do we find ways to reconnect to the joy that food can bring? How do we create spaces to think through these questions in community with each other?

One strategy that has worked well to foster these more critical conversations has been organizing community cooking classes that offer the opportunity to cook and eat together. We invite farmers to help make the connections between what runs in our rivers and what is served on our plates, to help us understand why purchasing foods grown without pesticides is important for our communities, and to forge connections between growers and consumers. We share the recipes and strategies of home cooks and professional chefs alike to drive home the reality that everyone has something to share. We invite doctors, nutritionists and community health workers to explain how nutrition-related chronic diseases like diabetes actually work in the body. And we open the floor for everyone to ask questions, share strategies and learn together. These cooking classes are one step in working towards the goal of building healthier communities through mindful practice. They provide a way to create community spaces for deep critique of systems and structures, while celebrating the knowledge present in our communities and helping us build healthier practices in relationship with food.

Truly being mindful means addressing structural causes in addition to individual behaviors. Becoming more aware of where our food comes from—building critical analysis behind healthy food choices—allows for self-determination, choice, empowerment and control within a deeply unhealthy food system. While mindful eating practice focuses on non-judgment, asserting that there are no right and wrong ways to eat, we feel that it is important to simultaneously build consciousness around food injustice so that people understand that their unhealthy eating practice, and possibly resultant poor health, are not just results of their bad behaviors. In shining light on the larger systems at play, it is possible to dissolve some of the guilt and shame that keeps many of us from feeling in control of our relationship to food. It is exciting and important to ask these questions. It is crucial to create spaces for communities to understand how food can be a tool in self-love and community building around healthy eating.

MINDFUL MENU

A Healthy Soul Food Feast for Four ♥ Blackened Tilapia

Mashed Sweet Potatoes ♥ Healthy Collard Greens

BLESSING
(Christian Grace)

The eyes of all wait upon you, O God,
And you give them their food in due season.
You open wide your hand
and fill all things living with plenteousness.
Bless, O Lord, these gifts to our use and us in your service;
relieve the needs of those in want and give us
thankful hearts for Christ's sake.
Amen.

Blackened Tilapia | YIELDS 4 PORTIONS
INGREDIENTS

1¼ lb tilapia fillets (5 oz each)

2 tsp blackening seasoning
   mixture

1½ tbsp paprika

1 tbsp onion powder

1 tsp ground black pepper

1 tsp dried basil

2 tsp canola oil

1 tbsp garlic powder

1 tbsp ground dried thyme

1 tsp cayenne pepper

1 tsp dried oregano

DIRECTIONS

1. Preheat skillet to high and add canola oil.
2. Rub tilapia on both sides with blackening seasoning.
3. Pan sear 2 to 3 minutes each side until desired doneness.

Mashed Sweet Potatoes | YIELDS 4 PORTIONS

INGREDIENTS

2 large sweet potatoes, peeled and cubed

½ cup nonfat sour cream

1 tbsp butter

¼ tsp kosher salt

¼ tsp cinnamon

1 tbsp brown sugar

DIRECTIONS

1. Place sweet potatoes in a large pot and cover with water.
2. Bring to a boil, reduce heat to medium and cook 10–15 minutes or until tender when pierced with a fork.
3. Drain and place potatoes in a large mixing bowl.
4. Mash with sour cream, butter, salt, cinnamon and brown sugar.

Healthy Collard Greens | YIELDS 8 PORTIONS

INGREDIENTS

8 oz smoked turkey necks

3 cans fat-free chicken broth

1 small red onion, diced

2 cloves garlic, minced

2 tsp olive oil

2–3 bunches of collard greens

salt and pepper to taste

crushed red pepper flakes (or jalapeños)—optional

DIRECTIONS

1. Rinse collard greens in the sink under running cold water.
2. Pick greens away from the stem.
3. Stack collard greens into several leaves on top of each other.
4. Roll the leaves together and cut collard green leaves into 1-inch-thick strips.
5. In a large pot, sauté diced red onion, garlic and olive oil.
6. Add equal amounts of water and chicken broth to large pot.
7. Add greens to pot, bring to boil and then reduce heat to simmer.
8. Cover with lid and continue to simmer for 1 hour.
9. In a small pot, boil turkey necks over medium-high heat until tender. Once turkey parts are tender, rinse and transfer to the pot containing your collard greens.
10. Once greens are tender, add salt and pepper to taste.
11. Add red pepper flakes or jalapeños (as much heat as you like).

URBAN AGRICULTURE AS A COMMUNITY-DEVELOPMENT STRATEGY
by Michael S. Easterling

Food systems are inherently complex. There are issues that deal directly with the soil and its condition tied to the land's historical use as well as its geography, access to water and other variables. Distribution, transportation, storage, insurance and budgetary concerns are also factors.

A food system embodies culture. The arts, science, oral history, gossip, celebration, grieving... life happens in the market. Fellowship and education build communities and hold them together. By participating in their community, people take ownership in a very real and direct way. The opportunity to have a positive impact on public health is tremendous, as well as to recreate intergenerational relationships.

Increasing interest in locally produced food, and the national push for better nutrition to combat the epidemics of obesity and diabetes, present unique opportunities to implement community-development strategies based on urban agriculture. In vacant lots throughout American cities to school gardens and urban rooftops, people across the country are choosing to grow food where they live, driven as much by the demand for lower-cost organic produce as by increasing awareness of the impact of food on well-being.

We have the challenge and opportunity to shift policy from corporate to local agriculture and our mindset from consumer to producer. There is a need for innovative approaches to urban farming that can maximize production on limited space, as well as for creative solutions that can facilitate healthy food access, entrepreneurial opportunities, environmental sustainability and stronger communities. How do we improve the environment through better farming? How do we enhance the safety and security of our food supply?

Opportunities for Black and Latino Leadership in the Local Food Movement

Lack of access to healthy food is an example of systemic racism that continues to plague urban communities. The demise of urban grocery stores had a reasonable economic justification, but that alone does not entirely explain what has happened in the absence of healthy options. The chronic diseases so prevalent in inner cities can be positively impacted by improved diet. Fresh fruits and vegetables are not available in much of the urban core, but alcohol and tobacco are everywhere.

The Organic Trade Association reports that retail sales of organic food in the U.S. rose from $3.6 billion in 1997 to $43 billion two decades later.[7] Much of this spending is in the high-end retail niche where organic products can cost double the conventional alternative. The local food movement both fuels and emerges from this increased economic activity. Virtually all of it occurs *outside* of impoverished urban areas. There is, however, increasing interest in viewing local organic food production as a viable pathway to reducing urban poverty.

Local food is often but not necessarily organic. It is more labor intensive and expensive to produce. Much of the work of planting, weeding and harvesting is done by hand or without industrial machines. Small or mid-sized food producers (what relatively few there still are), generally lack sophisticated marketing or distribution systems whether they grow organically or conventionally. They typically reach customers through a growing number of farmers' markets, cooperatives or community-supported agriculture (CSA) models.

Demand for local organic food is being driven by many factors including the national push for better nutrition to combat obesity and diabetes, rising energy prices that affect industrialized food systems, and recent food recalls due to widespread contamination of milk, eggs, spinach, beef and other products causing illness and death.

While everyone stands to benefit from increased access to affordable fresh produce, there are unique opportunities and challenges for African Americans and Latinos living in poor communities to become more engaged in the local food movement. African Americans and Latinos are disproportionately impacted by poverty in American cities. The foreclosure crisis continues to have a highly negative impact in their communities, resulting in hundreds and, in some cities, thousands of acres of vacant land and abandoned properties in areas where many poor families continue to live and work.

---

7   https://www.ota.com/news/press-releases/19681

Higher rates of unemployment, incarceration, chronic illness and morbidity are made worse by persistent educational underachievement and increasing social and spatial isolation (food deserts are defined as neighborhoods without any full-service grocery stores). These neighborhoods often have an overabundance of fast food or convenience stores that sell highly processed food, alcohol and tobacco products.

Constructing a Framework for Solutions

Many of us work in various ways to build sustainable communities. A wide range of influences—including what we do for a living, where and how we live, and our own personal beliefs—determine our definition of what that actually means. These influences are regulated by our values, which shape our perception and are at the core of how we see the world and our role in it.

Can we change the systems that govern our lives?

We can change the systems that govern our lives.

Spend a few moments inside of each sentence. Close your eyes and say each one out loud. Reflect on the emphasis and ultimately the state of mind that each one reinforces. The simple change from "Can we...?" to "We can..." reflects a fundamental shift in personal power and responsibility. "We can" also represents a more advantageous starting point when it comes to figuring out "how to."

A starting point to changing the systems that govern our lives is developing the habit of *systems thinking*. When you turn the lights on, for example, mentally trace the path of the current from the switch through the wiring in your home to the utility lines from your house to as far back as you can. Do the same when you turn on the water, eat, drive or any of myriad daily activities. Everything is the product and part of a larger system that brings it into being. The more that we are able to focus on how our daily lives connect to the complex systems that underlie them, the greater our capacity to begin to impact change within those systems.

Developing whole and healthy communities starts with recognition that every individual, group, institution and/or enterprise is connected to every other, whether we see or understand these connections or not. When we eat, we are part of the food system; when we have electricity, drive or take medicine, we are active participants in global industries. Yet we are typically not conscious of such participation in a way that could change the system, particularly given our consumer culture.

I am among those who believe that the key to unlocking opportunities lies in redefining our relationship with basic needs. While core needs have remained the same throughout the scope of human civilization, the context in which we relate to them has changed much in the last century. Survival—in short, whether or not we are able to access food, clothing and shelter—has become less dependent on one's ability to produce and more on being able to acquire or consume.

We now have the literal and figurative possibility of going back to our roots to help us inform the future. American communities were once self-sufficient, interdependent and sustainable. Individuals, families and members of social and professional networks started businesses that provided for the communities within which they lived and worked.

There is an opportunity for like-minded professionals in education, for example, to become more aware of what their role is in developing a local food system, while providing specialized information and/or resources to educators interested in playing a more direct role of incorporating food production into their learning environments. This content includes topics that are more focused on working in and with schools regardless of the program area, in addition to relevant food-system information.

I call the sum of these two functions an expression of "centralized decentralization." The better that we are able to perceive and understand the connections among ourselves as individuals, groups, institutions and enterprises, the more empowered we are to individually impact the whole community by appreciating the value of what we do in the moment. Values determine the nature and quality of our interactions with each other and with the world in which we live. They provide the moral frameworks for our conceptions of right and wrong, good and bad. Our behavior is ultimately the best reflection of our values.

Black and Latino communities stand to benefit the most from investing in local food production or urban agriculture as the basis of a holistic community-development strategy. Our participation and leadership in the local food movement holds the potential to increase educational outcomes, generate economic opportunity, and improve individual and community health. Opportunities exist to create school-based gardens that are tied to a standards-based curriculum and to workforce-development experiences. There are employment and entrepreneurial opportunities in the production, processing and distribution of food and related products, while also building relationships that increase civic engagement and promote healthy, active living. Perhaps most important, however, is the opportunity for self-determination in the cultivation of communities that are capable of sustaining themselves.

Cultivating Community

Organizations across the country are increasingly turning to community-based gardening to increase access to healthy food, introduce new programs in schools, and create social and economic opportunities for community residents. Schools have many built-in assets that make them natural hubs for urban agricultural projects. They hold the potential to serve as training grounds for a new generation of leadership that has been trained to pursue a triple bottom line of profit, social returns and environmental sustainability.

Food-producing gardens can be designed to fit the needs of any location, constituency, level of experience and budget. In addition to improving nutrition, the process of growing food for oneself or a family teaches patience, requires accountability and is emotionally rewarding. Small culinary gardens can even be developed into revenue-generating operations for either individual or community enterprises.

Community-based agriculture is inherently location specific, based on community and projects to create and reinforce relationships. A concentration of urban farms and the cluster of enterprises that would likely emerge from them hold the further potential to add to a region's draw as a tourist and commercial destination.

The economic reality that the freshest, highest-quality food is widely available to those who can pay the most for it tends to obfuscate the perspective that increased access to organic local food—let alone local food production—is a viable pathway to reducing urban poverty. This dynamic is perhaps the greatest challenge *and* the greatest opportunity in the emerging local food movement.

MINDFUL MENU

Oven-Baked "Fried" Chicken ♥ Orange-Glazed Carrots

BLESSING
(from the Moravian Church)

Come, Lord Jesus, our guest to be
And bless these gifts
Bestowed by Thee.
And bless our loved ones everywhere,
And keep them in Your loving care.

Oven-Baked "Fried" Chicken | YIELDS 8 PORTIONS

INGREDIENTS

1 cup fat-free milk or buttermilk

1 tsp poultry seasoning

1 cup cornflakes, crumbled

1½ tbsp onion powder

1½ tbsp garlic powder

2 tsp black pepper

2 tsp dried hot pepper, crushed

1 tsp ground ginger

8 (6-oz) pieces of boneless/ skinless chicken

a few shakes of paprika

vegetable or olive-oil spray

DIRECTIONS

1. Preheat oven to 350°F.
2. Add ½ teaspoon of poultry seasoning to milk.
3. Combine all other spices with cornflake crumbs and place in plastic bag. Pour milk into medium-sized bowl.

4. Wash chicken and pat dry. Dip chicken into milk and shake to remove excess. Quickly shake in bag with seasonings and crumbs, and remove the chicken from the bag.

5. Refrigerate chicken for 1 hour.

6. Remove chicken from refrigerator and sprinkle lightly with paprika for color.

7. Space chicken evenly on well-oil-sprayed baking pan.

8. Cover with aluminum foil and bake for 10 minutes. Remove foil and continue baking for another 8–10 minutes (internal temperature of 165°F). Meat will easily be pulled away from the bone with fork. *Crumbs will form crispy "skin."

Orange-Glazed Carrots | YIELDS 8 PORTIONS

INGREDIENTS

2 lb carrots

3 oz honey

1 cup fresh orange juice

1 tbsp unsalted butter

kosher salt and freshly ground black pepper

1 tbsp fresh dill leaves

DIRECTIONS

1. Cut a 1-inch chunk off one end of a carrot at an angle. Roll the carrot a quarter turn and cut another 1-inch chunk at an angle. Continue rolling and cutting all of the carrots.

2. Combine the carrots and orange juice in a large saucepan. Add enough water to just cover the carrots. Add the butter and ¼ teaspoon each of salt and pepper.

3. Bring to a boil, and then reduce the heat to maintain a steady simmer. Cook 5 minutes or until fork tender. Remove carrots and reserve.

4. Cook remaining liquid until it has reduced to a glaze (about 10 minutes).

5. Pour and mix glaze with carrots. Top with the dill and serve.

BUEN PROVECHO, SOBREMESAS AND LESSONS LEARNED AT THE DINNER TABLE

by Victor Ruiz

Growing up Puerto Rican in a mostly white and black housing project in Cleveland, Ohio, was very difficult. Making fun of my accent, hair, food, music and other cultural markers provided the children in my neighborhood with a lot of entertainment. They enjoyed themselves but it was terrifying for me. My first act of disowning my culture was giving up beans. For those of you who are familiar with the Puerto Rican way of life, rice and beans are at the center of the food universe. For a poor family, sometimes rice and beans is all that they have. When I gave up eating those staples, I created financial and social stress for my mother. A Puerto Rican who does not eat beans is an embarrassment to other Puerto Ricans! Such a person is described as an elitist who is not proud to be Puerto Rican. I can only imagine my mom's humiliation at parties when I would bypass the beans at the buffet line. I do remember the whispers, especially from other family members: *"El nene de Margo no come habichueles. ¿Quièn se cree que es el?"* ("Margo's son doesn't eat beans. Who does he think he is?")

It wasn't until I reached adulthood that I fully understood the ramifications of my behavior. It wasn't just beans that I rejected, but my entire culture. I was also rejecting speaking Spanish, Latin music, even being seen in public with my Puerto Rican mother. Years of ethnic discrimination led me to minimize and despise my very being, while accepting that the dominant culture was superior and I was inferior!

While being called a "bean eater" was traumatic for me as a child, rejecting the work that went into those beans was even worse. My mother, who suffered a lot to ensure that we did not go to bed hungry, took tremendous pride in her cooking. Compliments about her food were like gold medals, badges of pride that made her happy in an otherwise difficult life. My rejection of *habichuelas*, a simple and inexpensive food, was a rebuff to her, the family and my people. It was a rejection of their sacrifices, talents and love of family.

Latinos approach eating as more than an act necessary for daily living. Food and eating is an experience tied to our culture, values and way of life. There is also a sincere belief that food is to be enjoyed with others, and that such experiences are more important than the food itself. As I got older I was able to understand, appreciate and revere my cultural traditions around food, including saying *Buen provecho* during a meal. This phrase is said to someone who is eating and difficult to translate into English. To say that it means "have a good meal" or "bon appétit" does not fully explain the phrase. The words express respect and reverence for the experience taking place. *Buen provecho* is more like a blessing, a sincere wish that the experience of eating the meal will be positive and nourishing. It represents an acknowledgment that there is a bond between food and people, coupled with an understanding that the act of eating does not tell the full story: the sacrifices made to get the food, the hard work and love that went into preparing it, and the pride that goes with both. *Buen provecho* is returned with *buen provecho* or a simple *gracias*.

I also learned to understand that the experience around the meal table has a name, *sobremesa*, another hard-to-translate notion that literally means "over the table." *Sobremesas* are the unrushed exchanges, conversations and overall time spent with others during a meal, which will likely continue well past the food having been eaten. These *sobremesas* are much more than conversations; they shape values, traditions and people.

I am able to understand the impact of families eating together from personal experience. When I came to Cleveland at age 5, my mother did not work and we ate every meal together. At the meal table we talked about our day, my mom reminded us about our homework and we argued about going to church, as well as discussing other family matters. The practice of family meals continued until I was 10 when my brother started kindergarten and my mom took her first job. While the food itself was still amazing, it was now waiting for us on the stove when we got home from school. My brother and I would just eat when we got hungry and more than likely do so in front of the TV. Hot breakfasts eventually became cold cereal on the run, and complex Puerto Rican delicacies eventually became meals that were easy to microwave. As we grew up, we all grew apart. My brother eventually started having behavioral issues at school and home, I became a recluse consumed by books and music while avoiding the world beyond my bedroom, and my mother worked multiple jobs to avoid falling below our working-poor status.

I know that my family's issues cannot be completely attributed to the loss of family mealtime. We were a typical family dealing with the impact of poverty, single-motherhood, domestic violence and other issues. However, not having our dinner table time together meant that our coping mechanism, therapy, venting place and support system were gone. Instead of dealing with it together, we dealt with it by ourselves—alone. My brother acted out and became involved in the juvenile-criminal-justice system at an early age. It took my mother decades to break free of a vicious cycle of violent relationships. I became a father at age 17. Our family seemed more like three individuals who happened to be tied by blood and we yearned for something new and better.

In my junior year at college, I took a communications class with a professor who was engaged in a major research project documenting the effect of shared family meals on social behavior and academic performance. I found this simple concept fascinating— that something as basic as family meals can help children be successful in school and contribute to their communities. Recent studies support my professor's early research and show that Latino children are more likely to eat meals with their families than black and white children. Sadly, that number has declined with each generation. There is overwhelming evidence supporting the benefits of family mealtime, according to a report by the research organization, Child Trends (www.childtrends.org). When families eat together, children are less likely to engage in risky social and sexual behavior or substance abuse. They get better grades in school and have healthier eating and dietary habits (including lower rates of obesity and eating disorders).[8]

After graduating from college, my wife, son and I moved into an apartment and were responsible for creating our own family traditions. While the meals were not prepared according to Puerto Rican culinary traditions, we made a point to eat together. Our family grew as did our careers. Life got busier and eventually I started missing many dinners.

---

8   http://www.childtrends.org/wp-content/uploads/2012/09/96_Family_Meals.pdf

While my job was and is meaningful, I regret that I missed so much of my children's lives. Fortunately, my wife held the family together and continued having dinners around the table. I missed conversations about my son's struggles in high school, and was not able to observe how my two boys interacted with each other or treated their sister and mother. Those circumstances could have led to teachable moments, when children learn from their parents and vice versa. I wish that I could go back, manage my time better, reprioritize and better understand what truly matters.

I'm still not home every evening for dinner and our children are older and busy with activities. However, we've come to cherish those times when we do eat together. Sunday brunches are more common now as are late-night ice-cream runs in the summer. One of my favorite new traditions is our "sparkling water with lime" competitions when my children and I compete to see who can make the most sour sparkling water with limes. We sit at the table and pass around our cups and taste each one. I also love cheese tastings with my daughter. Every few weeks I buy different cheeses and sit with her, tasting and talking about what we like and dislike about each one. What may seem like mundane activities are valuable times to intentionally build family and grow together; these are the basic building blocks of community.

We must come to terms with the reality that our communities sometimes are called into service as surrogate families. In this role, communities often falter, approaching children from a limited, transactional perspective, viewing them as relatively helpless victims to be moved passively along pipelines and past milestones, mistaking them as mere system outputs along a pathway to independence that is desired but seldom achieved. Unless we go deeper, helping to inspire, empower and transform our young, negative cycles promise to continue unabated. A few simple solutions can have a tremendous impact in our children's lives:

♥ Create innovative opportunities to share meals together. We know that children eat many meals away from home (at schools, after-school programs, summer camps, with friends et al.), yet as a result of rushed schedules, staff shortages, irresponsible supervision, and undesirable and unhealthy food, these meals leave lasting negative impressions. We have an opportunity to turn school lunchtime into school mealtimes, when schools invite parents and community members to eat meals with students. Instead of giving them 20 minutes to swallow their food, this time can be extended so that there are meaningful exchanges—*sobremesas*—between students, families and mentors. The same practice can be extended, for example, to daycares, summer meal programs and churches. Instead of the meal program being transactional, it can become transformative.

♥ Produce a comprehensive marketing campaign that promotes the benefits of eating meals together. Partners could include the Ad Council, major food companies, healthcare systems and others directly invested in family health. Elements of the campaign can include prompts and questions to guide the mealtime discussion.

I've learned so much about my family during our *sobremesas*, about their passions and dreams, frustrations and joys, and values. We talk about society and how we engage with and in it. We discuss race (important for our mixed-race family), gender, sexuality, poverty and wealth, education and all of the other issues we face in everyday life. We educate our children and help shape their beliefs, and in turn we learn from them. While these conversations can occur at any time, mealtimes give us a specific reason to gather together and relax. When we nourish our bodies, we nourish our souls.

Sobremesas have become a regular practice in my personal and work life. Many of my professional meetings and interactions with friends and extended family include some sort of meal that gives us a chance to know one another more personally. What may have in the past been a strategic networking event, plea for money or obligatory family visit are now sincere attempts to build partnerships, friendships and strong family bonds. I know that eating a meal around a table is not going to solve all of our societal issues, but we often make solutions overly complicated. As data overwhelmingly support the positive impact of eating family meals together, then we can—with little resources and risk—expand that practice to all aspects of our daily lives. If it works for the family unit, it will work for neighborhoods, communities, cities and states.

We must be intentional about creating opportunities and environments where our children and families can thrive and achieve happiness. We must also be ambassadors of Dr. King's vision of beloved community that can only occur when human beings have meaningful interactions, when strangers can validate our hopes and embrace one another as partners in this journey called life. These types of interactions are not automatic and must be taught. In its simplest form, the beloved community is made up of people loving each other and expressing that love through acts of kindness. While sometimes not easy, it is achievable and starts at home. Blessings on your journey y *buen provecho.*

MINDFUL MENU

French Toast Casserole

BLESSING
(Christian Grace)

Bless, O Lord, this food we are about to eat; and we pray to you, O God, that it may be good for our body and soul; and if there be any poor creature hungry or thirsty walking along the road, send them into us that we can share the food with them, just as you share your gifts with all of us.

French Toast Casserole | YIELDS 4–6 PORTIONS

INGREDIENTS

8 slices whole wheat bread

1 medium apple (preferably Fuji) diced

4 oz low-fat cream cheese, room temperature

1¼ cups unsweetened soymilk

1 cup liquid egg whites

2 tbsp maple syrup

¾ tbsp butter

¼ tsp cinnamon

¼ tsp vanilla extract

1 tsp brown sugar

DIRECTIONS

1. Preheat oven to 350°F.
2. Spray an eight-inch by eight-inch baking dish with olive-oil spray.
3. Place bread cubes evenly along the bottom of the dish.
4. Sprinkle diced apple evenly over the bread.

5. In a blender, combine all other ingredients (cream cheese through brown sugar in the list above). Blend until lump-free and smooth.

6. Pour mixture over the bread and apple. Make sure bread is soaked in the liquid mixture. If needed, toss lightly to coat.

7. Bake in the oven for about 45 minutes, until egg mixture is pretty firm and cooked through.

8. Let cool slightly and cut into eight squares.

NAVIGATING BALANCE AND PEACE IN MOTHERHOOD

by Brealynn Lee

Giving birth to a child, especially your first, is a life-altering experience. A new mother cycles through a whirlwind of emotions from fear to happiness to the deepest expression of love. New mothers are often subject to a steady undercurrent of anxiety caused by lack of sleep, a hormonal reset, worries about balancing baby with work and misgivings about the ability to be a good mother. Breastfeeding can amp up the anxiety, especially when baby and mother have problems with the process.

Breastfeeding can be frustrating, especially in the beginning when trying to get the baby to latch on properly and suck. Some mothers become frustrated when they cannot produce enough milk. I chose to breastfeed my baby, but it took almost a week until I could because she was premature and my milk supply was not ready. I felt like a failure as a mother because I couldn't feed my baby. The hospital's lactation consultant helped tremendously by giving me the keys to successful breastfeeding. I understand that my experience was common, that I was not alone. Once breastfeeding has been mastered, many mothers find that it provides the most relaxing and peaceful moments of their days. Breastfeeding is a naturally mindful experience. The baby and mother are quietly and completely focused on each other. The child is fully present while sucking its sustenance, partaking of the ultimate mindful meal combining gratitude, perfect nutrition and loving, meaningful human bonding leading to whole-person development. The connection between nursing mother and child provides an ideal foundation for mindful nutrition over a lifespan.

Beside providing a periodic oasis of calm, breastfeeding offers many health benefits to the child and mother. Breast milk is the best thing for your child to help fight off sickness; breastfed babies have a lower risk of ear infections, asthma and respiratory infections. Nursing also helps mommies burn calories, resulting in quick post-pregnancy weight loss, while breastfeeding mothers have a lower risk of type 2 diabetes and breast cancer. Breastfeeding also offers financial benefits; just think of the money being saved by not buying expensive formula.

A healthy diet is also key to a successful breastfeeding experience. Remember that you are producing nourishment for your child; the better your health the better quality of milk that you produce. Being mindful of what you eat puts you in the best position to manage your own well-being as well as your child's.

- ♥ You will need to eat plenty of the following:
  - Fresh fruits and vegetables, with lots of leafy greens.
  - Protein such as lean meats, eggs, salmon and other fish low in mercury.
  - Grains like rice and whole-grain bread add much-needed fiber.
  - Milk and low-fat dairy, such as yogurt and cheese.
  - Water! Water! Water! At least 62 ounces minimum a day.

- ♥ Sleep is also a key factor to successful breastfeeding. Your body needs to rest in order to produce milk. It can be a challenge with your newborn, but can be done.
  - Find a quiet place.
  - Sleep when the baby sleeps.
  - Listen to soothing music.
  - Keep one of the baby's blankets with you while you sleep. The scent from the baby on the blanket promotes milk production.

- ♥ Relax and keep calm. When you sit with your baby for a feeding, take a few minutes to center yourself. Close your eyes. Take a few deep breaths. When your child is feeding, continue to focus on your steady breathing as well as the baby's.

- ♥ Many mothers use a breastfeed pump to allow a break for themselves from bottle feeding. Add an extra pumping session to your day if you can. The more you pump, the more you supply because your body makes as much as your child wants and needs. Let the time you are pumping be another chance to practice mindfulness. Gaze at your baby or hold the baby's blanket to help you relax and focus.

♥ Flaxseed, fenugreek and milk thistle are awesome natural supplements that promote milk production. Fenugreek is an herb and seed used to increase milk flow, mostly used in pill and tea form. It can be found alone with milk thistle in the vitamin and supplement section of your local drugstore or wellness store; you can also find it online. Flaxseed not only helps with milk production but also provides a great source of fiber. I love to use it in my baking. I've included a recipe for flaxseed cookies—a great way to get your flaxseed quota. Not only are the cookies delicious, but they are a great healthy snack for the whole family. Have two or three cookies with a bottle of water before pumping.

The day-to-day activities of motherhood can take a toll on anyone's physical and mental health. Dealing with the fatigue, hunger and stress of having a brand new addition to your family can be downright overwhelming. Prime example: It's 3 a.m. and your new bundle of joy is sounding the alarm again that he or she is ready for the next feeding. You're operating on maybe an hour and a half of sleep, trying to navigate in the direction of the crib or bassinet in the dark because you just don't have the strength to find the light switch—which leads to your finding said crib with your foot, so now you're tired, blind and in pain. Does any of this sound familiar? If it does, you're not alone; this is exactly what happened to me just 48 hours after bringing my infant daughter home from the hospital. Not only was I tired because I kept popping up every 10 to 15 minutes to check on the baby, I was hungry and in need of a shower. On top of all that, I had the additional pain of a caesarean incision. Who wouldn't be a little stressed with all of that going on, right? A lot of mothers will agree that what I just described is a common scenario in the day-to-day of newborn management. But don't panic; I have good news. There are several ways to obtain balance in the adventurous profession of motherhood. Mindful practices can help manage stress and anxiety.

Stress and Frustration
Stress and frustration or, as I like to refer to them, "The Mommy Blues," were what I had to deal with as soon as my little one entered the world. My baby girl was born prematurely at 37 weeks with a collapsed lung and an enlarged heart—talk about stressful moments! I

had to figure out how to manage and alleviate my stress in order to be supportive to my baby. One thing I learned from our two-week stay in the hospital is that stress will stifle healing in the body. Having a newborn can be overwhelming even for a seasoned mother, especially if you have other children to tend to as well. I learned some ways to cope with the multiple demands of new motherhood and it is my mission to share what I know with others. Here are a few rules and tips to help you achieve peace and sanity.

If mom is not happy, *no one* is happy. When you are stressed and frustrated, it spreads throughout the home. Mothers are the heartbeat of the family and when the heartbeat is erratic the entire body is disturbed. So how do we minimize the stress? By getting our spouse, partner or family members involved. Try to identify what is triggering your stress and fueling your frustration, and your insights with those in your support system. Using mindful techniques, pay close attention to your movements throughout the day. When feeling anxious, stop, breathe deeply, still your mind and listen to your inner voice.

Communicate with those who are supporting you. Let them know what insights you gleaned in your mindful moments. You can practice a mindful meditation while in the bubble bath, just before lying down for a nap or before you have an afternoon snack. We have to understand that even supermom needs help from time to time. So hand the baby to your spouse or other support person and take a moment for yourself.

Find a nice spot in your home to be alone. Set up an area where you can be comfortable with very minimal traffic. We underestimate the beauty of a few minutes of silence, which will help to still your racing mind for just a moment and regroup. Make use of those awesome Lamaze breathing techniques you learned, similar to those of meditation. We use an awareness of our breath to calm ourselves.

If you are able to leave the house for an hour or two, use this time to pamper yourself. Get your hair or nails done, or get a massage. You can also go for a run or to the gym as long as your doctor has cleared you to do so. A lot of women find working out as a way to relieve stress.

Get the family involved, especially older children. Let your children plan and make their own lunches and snacks for the week. Assist the child or children in researching lunch and snack choices; this allows them the opportunity to make healthy meals and takes one task off your hands for the week. And for you first-time moms, I haven't forgotten about you; have your spouse or family help by creating healthy quick meals that you can grab or warm up without the hassle of standing over a hot stove cooking. These tips will give time to spend relaxing and enjoying your little one.

You need sleep! Yes I know it's hard to get a solid eight hours in with a newborn, but please try. Sleep is a key element to killing stress. Sleep when the baby sleeps; that way you can train your body to be on schedule with the baby, thus eliminating the stress of having your sleep interrupted. If you become exhausted, let someone know and allow them to watch the little one so that you can recharge your batteries.

The Most Important Rule of All! What you eat plays a big part in your wellness. So let's explore seven superfoods that help relieve stress.

Foods	Benefits
BLUEBERRIES	The antioxidants in blueberries aid the brain in producing dopamine, a chemical that promotes memory and calm moods.
LEAFY GREENS	Dark leafy greens like spinach, kale and turnip greens are rich in folate, which helps your body produce mood-regulating neurotransmitters including serotonin and dopamine.
DARK CHOCOLATE	Chocolate has anandamide, a neurotransmitter produced in the brain that temporarily blocks feelings of pain and depression.
AVOCADOS	Avocados are packed with potassium and vitamins E and B (including folate), which help with stress and milk production.
ORGANIC PISTACHIOS	Two or more servings of this power nut can promote lower vascular constriction during stress.
ALASKAN WILD SALMON	Salmon is rich in omega-3 fatty acids and DHA, which play a big part in emotional wellness.
TURKEY	This is a good source of tryptophan that your body converts into serotonin. Research shows that mothers who consume foods containing tryptophan regularly have a more pleasant mood.

Returning to Work

There are many aspects of new motherhood that can be stressful and, for some moms, returning to work is the biggest stressor of all. I must admit the hardest thing that I had to face after giving birth was returning to work. The first day back I was a wreck but got myself together, and fought the urge to pick up the phone and call the nanny a hundred times to see what my little angel was doing. I think that if I didn't have a game plan for returning to work, I would have been stressed beyond functionality.

The Game Plan

Let your employer know as early as possible how much time you plan to spend on maternity leave. Any special request or accommodation you may need should be expressed at this time. For instance, I needed a place to pump my breast milk when I was at work. I also had to adjust my schedule to be able to pick my little one up from the nanny. Be upfront about what you need to make your return smooth.

1. Communicate with your support team regarding duties needed to be performed around the home in order to make your return to work easy on the household. Do you need someone to cook dinner, put on a load of laundry or load the dishwasher? Be clear about what you need to keep unnecessary stress to a minimum. Get the family involved; you will be surprised at how willing older siblings are to help make the home life flow smoothly.

2. Make a meal plan to help manage the time you spend with your spouse and family. Everyone has to eat, and just because you are working again and dealing with a new addition does not mean that you can't eat good, healthy meals. A lot of mothers fall victim to the lure of fast food. We don't want that to happen because that will destroy all of your efforts to make milk and stay mindful and stress-free. Take the time to create a two-week meal plan twice a month and make sure that you have the ingredients you need in your pantry.

3. Plan ahead if your child will be going to daycare or if you will have someone in your home to provide care. Take the four weeks before returning to work to research, interview and choose a provider. Discuss in detail what you expect for your child's care. Be detailed in how you want things done for your child from feedings to nap time. Make sure to put those

requirements in writing and list any special needs that your child may have, such as a food allergy.

4. Relax at work. When you feel that pull of separation anxiety, pull out a pic of your little one and take a few minutes to close your eyes and breathe mindfully. Just remember that when you're finished with your workday, a sweet little person will be waiting for you. I remember walking into my home and my baby reaching for me, all excited. It was best feeling ever, and I take that memory with me every day to work.

Whether you are a new mother, or an experienced one, the first few months after giving birth can be challenging and stressful. Taking care of your nutritional needs, and doing so mindfully, will help you and your baby thrive.

MINDFUL MENU

Mommy Milk Cookies ♥ Flaxseed Tea

BLESSING
(Yogi blessing)

Brahman, the Supreme Divinity, is the ritual. Brahman is the offering, Brahman is he who offers to the fire that is also Brahman. By seeing Brahman in all actions, one realizes Brahman. May the soul of the universe be pleased. Om, peace, peace, peace.

Mommy Milk Cookies

INGREDIENTS

8 tbsp salted butter	5 tbsp flaxseed
½ cup white sugar	5 tbsp brewer's yeast
¼ cup packed light-brown sugar	1½ cups all-purpose flour
1 tsp vanilla	½ tsp baking soda
2 tbsp hot water	¼ tsp salt
2 eggs	¾ cup chocolate chips or chocolate chunks

DIRECTIONS

1. Preheat the oven to 350°F. Melt the butter in the microwave for 35 to 45 seconds; it should be melted but not hot.
2. Using a hand or stand mixer, cream the butter with the sugars until smooth. Add the vanilla and the eggs; beat on low speed

until just incorporated; 10 to 15 seconds should get the job done. Make sure that you don't overbeat.

3. Combine the flour, baking soda, flaxseed, brewer's yeast and salt. Mix until crumbles form. Use your hands to press the crumbles together into a dough to form one large ball that is easy to handle (right at the stage between "wet" and "dry" dough). Add the chocolate chips and incorporate with your hands.

4. Use a standard cookie scoop for your desired number of cookies and place on a cookie sheet. Bake for eight to 10 minutes until the cookies look puffy and slightly golden. Warning: Do not overbake! This advice is probably written on every cookie recipe everywhere, but this is to keep the cookies soft. Take them out even if they look like they're not done. They'll be pale and puffy, yet oh so chewy.

5. Cool on the pan for a good 30 minutes. The cookies will sink down and turn into these dense, buttery, soft cookies that will make you the coolest mom ever. They should stay soft for many days if kept in an airtight container. The raw cookie dough can be frozen as well as the baked cookies.

Flaxseed Tea

Steep 1 teaspoon of ground seeds, 2 tablespoons of meal or one tea bag in about 1 cup of boiling water for 10 to 15 minutes with loose tea or two to four minutes with a tea bag. Strain the hot liquid and, if desired, add some cinnamon or honey for extra flavor.

FOOD AS MEDICINE

by Jonathan, Sr., and Elizabeth Michaelle Rinehart

"We are a part of everything that is beneath us, above us, and around us.... Our past is our present, our present is our future, and our future is seven generations past and present. Let us be the ancestors our descendants will thank."

—Winona LaDuke

As Native American (Anishinaabek) people, we use the gifts of our earth mother to help us. We call the elements our medicine. These are our prayers; they carry our positive thoughts and energy. Our medicine can be tangible and used to heal and restore balance within our bodies. The medicine wheel, which represents life as a continuous circle, teaches us about these medicines and life itself. Eva Petoskey states, "In the Anishinaabek worldview all things are interrelated. The medicine wheel incorporates the Powers of the Four Directions and the interrelatedness of all things" *(Traditional Teachings and the Medicine Wheel, The Powers of the Four Directions, 2006)*. Each medicine is associated with a direction: East is represented by Séma (tobacco); South is Gishkiy (cedar); West is Pkwënézgen (sage); and North is Wishpëmishkos (sweet grass). Our medicine can be laid down, burnt or eaten. Each method is used for different purposes: sustenance, healing, cleansing, prayer, and to demonstrate our gratitude.

The medicine wheel teaches us about ourselves and our relationship to others. Our whole being is made up of four interconnect-

ed parts: mental, physical, emotional and spiritual. These parts are not separate. The east/yellow direction represents our mental self (how we think), and is associated with birth and rebirth or the acquisition of new knowledge. This is where we have to reconcile and accept ourselves as physical and spiritual beings, and never deny ourselves as a spiritual part of nature. The south/red direction, shows us the representation of our physical self (physical health and well-being). This area encompasses youth, strength, heart, generosity and sensitivity. In the western direction, represented by the color black, we recognize our emotional self (how we feel). The gifts of this direction are contemplation, deep inner thoughts and the unknown. Finally, we look to the northern direction, represented by white, like the hair of our elders. This reminds us to keep our spirit and heart strong. This direction's gifts are wisdom, insight, moderation and justice necessary for survival—physical, emotional and mental survival from loneliness and depression. The entire medicine wheel converges at the center, with all of the colors and directions touching to represent the delicate balance within us all. If one area is unbalanced, our entire being is off balance.

For Native Americans, traditional food is central to our well-being. It is a gift from the Creator that feeds and sustains us. We also consider it to be medicine that has the ability to heal us. Our traditional foods are connected to the medicine wheel because it also represents our seasons—whichever season brings the food is a gift from that direction. In the past, our ancestors were mindful when we harvested, prepared and ate food. We laid our Séma (tobacco) down when we planted seeds, and again at harvest with prayers and gratitude for their sacrifice. We cared for our growing plants by protecting them, singing and talking to them. We thanked the animal for its sacrifice. We prepared meals with good thoughts and feelings, never while we were angry or sad. We knew that we harness and give energy and were careful of where we deposited negative energy.

Being mindful members of the Anishinaabek means recognizing that our traditional food has a story, a way it came to be. The stories vary from tribe to tribe and each tribe's stories are accepted by other tribes as truth. For Woodland tribes, corn sprouted after a hunter's vision of a woman who offered it as a gift, which he found upon awakening. Maple syrup began as a gift flowing freely from the trees, yet was quickly diluted after people grew too lazy to do anything but sit under the trees with their mouths open. When we know the story, we learn how to appreciate and interact with that form of life. We learn both how we fit and the hard lessons that the story's characters went through to maintain balance. Some may view this is fantastical, but for Anishinaabek these stories are true, such as the one Michaelle shares about her grandmother:

> One day after school, I walked in the door and a waft of the distinct smell of Indian corn flooded my nose. My grandmother sang as she stirred the huge silver pot on the stovetop. I peered inside to see what phase the cooking was at. It was dark. The ashes were still at work softening the hulls of the kernels. My grandmother said that to know when it was done, it had to look like mud. Soon she called, "Who's going to help me wash this corn?" I ran to my room to exchange my school clothes for raggedy ones, and followed her to the backyard where she had a mesh table set up to wash the corn. After emptying the contents onto the screen, she grabbed the hose and proceeded to rinse, while I gently rubbed the corn between my hands. She told me that when I did this, I was to be mindful of my thoughts and do it with joy. It was hard work and I started to complain. She told me how much easier it is now with the screen than when she was little. My great-grandfather would have her kneel in a creek and wash the corn in a specially designed black ash basket. After her story, she encouraged me to sing as I washed: "Dum-na-boo! Dum-na-boo!" I giggled as she sang and together we joyfully washed the corn.

Every time Michaelle tells that story, her memory returns her to her childhood. It has become a fiber woven into the web of her existence. As an adult, she still makes corn soup because it is one of the legacies left by her grandmother. This is how Anishinaabek people teach—through everyday events and stories. There is not a specific time and place like traditional school. In effect, corn is a vessel for a much bigger lesson: prepare food with love and gratitude.

Jonathan has many positive memories of cooking with his mother. One in particular stands out in his mind:

> As Anishinaabek, we have always celebrated Thanksgiving. Before colonization, it was a celebration and expression of gratitude for the bounty of the fall harvest. Although assimilation caused our diet at Thanksgiving to shift from things like venison and wild rice to turkey and stuffing, my mom still made it the best! She would sing old traditional songs

in the kitchen as she waltzed around stirring and chopping the ingredients. Like an elegant symphony, she composed the most delicious Thanksgiving feast for us. I desired to be able to cook like her and worked hard to pay attention, sometimes asking her specific questions. A time came after my mother's passing when it was now my responsibility to prepare the Thanksgiving meal. I was nervous. Did I pay enough attention to my mother? Did I remember what she taught me? As I sat there wondering how I was going to pull it off, I started to hear a small voice instructing me: "Chop the celery." I got up and began following the instructions: "Don't forget to salt the inside of the turkey." Soon I felt as though my hands were operating through an unseen force. I felt her with me. "Sing." I began singing the songs of old that she sang as she cooked. "Open the chicken broth." With her voice and presence, the meal crescendoed until at last it was time to eat. Tears welled in my eyes as I tasted the first bite and I felt like a boy again, sitting with my mother at a beautiful feast. I was fed more than physically. My spirit was fed through the presence of my mother who had long since passed this physical world; I was at peace emotionally, realizing that she had never left. The food and experience were my medicine.

These are examples of healthy relationships to food, and demonstrate how Anishinaabek view the interconnectedness between ourselves and the food we eat. Unfortunately, however, through assimilation and because of genocidal practices, our diets have shifted to the modern Western diet, which has changed food from medicine to a poison that wreaks havoc on our bodies. The typical American diet causes diseases and illness like diabetes and heart disease, which rank in the top five diseases causing mortalities in AI/AN (American Indian or Alaska Native). In fact, according to 2007–2009 death statistics from Indian Health Service, American Indians are 3.1 times more likely to die from diabetes than all other races in the United States.[9]

Some of the reasons for these illnesses and ailments stem from an imbalance in one of the medicine wheel's four quadrants: phys-

---

9   https://www.ncbi.nlm.nih.gov/pmc/articles/PMC4035870/

ical, emotional, mental and spiritual. If one is physically malnourished, it is going to affect how that individual is feeling mentally, emotionally and spiritually. If the malnourishment is emotional, then the individual may manifest physical symptoms and feel weak mentally and spiritually. This is why it is imperative that Anishinaabek return to the ways of our ancestors, directly addressing the four quadrants of the medicine wheel that also address our entire being. We need to go back and relearn the stories about where our food came from, and discover how to treat and consume it to obtain optimal balance.

Perhaps the first way to tap into food's medicinal qualities is through abstinence. With fasting and vision quests, an individual sacrifices a physical desire to be fed to demonstrate humility when approaching the spirit realm. The spirits then communicate through dreams and visions. All four quadrants of the medicine wheel are addressed when fasts are completed. Through fasting, physical bodies are offered digestive respite, allowing the body additional energy for healing to take place that would otherwise be used to aid digestion. Mentally, it allows a quiet time to focus and think, and reflect on the reconciliation between the spiritual and physical self. The spirit is strengthened through discipline and self-control. Emotionally, it strengthens the heart, recognized as the center of emotion. These are the benefits of the quest itself, but there are also protocols that must be reclaimed as well.

Traditionally, fasts are broken by being fed a strawberry by an elder. The strawberry for the Anishinaabe culture is a sacred berry. We consider it the heart berry because of its shape and the healing properties that directly affect the heart as well as cleanse the blood. The strawberry's medicinal traits are further rooted in our belief that the shape of our food instructs us in its medicinal property and the part of the body that the food will benefit. In our language, the strawberry is called *Ode'min*. 'Ode' means heart and 'min' means small and globular, or berry. While many people only eat the red portion of the berry, we see the whole fruit as an important life-giving substance. George Martin, a respected elder in the Anishinaabek community, said that failure to eat the entire berry—leaves and all—shows disrespect. And in fact, our elders tell us that most of its nutrients are in the leaf tops. Being hand-fed by an elder reflects our dependence on others in a collective society. The berry is touched to an individual's lips four times to represent the four quadrants of the medicine wheel.

As important as the berry is, we also revere water's role in our story. Predating European contact, Anishinaabek already recognized the importance of acknowledging water. Much of our thoughts on water have been echoed by author Dr. Masuru Emoto, who made it his life's work to study the effects of energy, words and music on water. He believed that, like the water, we need positive interactions to induce positive emotions, which affect the physical body. Dr. Emoto states in his book, *The Hidden Messages in Water,* "Words are an expression of the soul. And the condition of our soul is very likely to have an enormous impact on the water that composes as much as 70 percent of our body, and this impact will in no small way affect our bodies."[10] As Anishinaabek, we sing to the water to honor its ability to heal, and the gift of life that it brings. We acknowledge as people that we are brought into this world through a sac filled with water. It protected us in our mother's womb. Therefore we are to appreciate and protect water. One of the ways we do this is in our water ceremonies. We thank the water through a song by Doreen Day that expresses, "We love you. We thank you. We respect you."[11] By offering this blessing, we transform water to medicine that provides healing to our bodies, which in turn affects the balance of the entire being.

Food is medicine. In the beginning, the Creator made all things work together to bring balance and harmony. There are many lessons that need to be learned or relearned. Some come from our elders' teachings, some through the spirit within ourselves and some directly from living things. When we watch animals such as the bear, they show us where to find life-giving sustenance and medicine when they forage for food and dig for roots.

Plants also communicate what they need. When their leaves are wilting, we know that they need water. If not thriving, they may be communicating that they would like to be moved. When thriving, we know that they are content and to continue what we are doing to help them. We can also glean lessons from plants in the manner that they grow. The strawberries are connected through a complex root

10   Emoto, Masaru, 1943–. *The Hidden Messages in Water.* Hillsboro, OR: Beyond Words Pub., 2004.
11   http://www.motherearthwaterwalk.com/?attachment_id=2244

system that stemmed from an original, but all are connected and can be traced back to the mother plant, which sends out vines that develop roots and become another plant. We are like the strawberry plants: not separate beings but rather one strand in the web of life. We are interconnected with each form of life.

We are all related. Traditionally, this is how we—as Anishinaabek people—think about our relationship to other forms of life whether fellow men, four-legged or winged creatures, plants or the elements of earth, water, air and fire. We acknowledge our relationship to our ancestors, and our responsibility to future descendants. What kind of ancestors we will be depends on how we live our lives presently on mother earth. Food is medicine, and how we interact with it is vital to bringing forth the medicinal properties that provide balance both to ourselves as well as our part in the circle of life. In this act, we have to be mindful.

MINDFUL MENU

Native Recipe for Meat Stew

BLESSING
(Water Song Prayer[12])

Nee-beh Gee Zah- gay-e-go

Gee Me-gwetch- wayn-nee-me-go

Gee-Zah Wayn ne-me-go

Translation:

Water, we love you. We thank you. We respect you.

Native Sweet Meat Chili | YIELDS 6–8 PORTIONS

INGREDIENTS

1 lb ground venison/buffalo

1 cup raisins

2 cups diced apples

2 tbsp maple syrup

1 cup chopped walnuts (optional)

4 tbsp vegetable oil

salt and pepper to taste

DIRECTIONS

1. Heat oil in a large pan, add ground meat and cook over medium heat until it is thoroughly cooked. Stir to prevent sticking.
2. Stir in other ingredients; simmer until fruit is warm.

---

12 Ibid.

CALLING UPON THE WISDOM OF THE FIVE ELEMENTS

by Kevin John Fong

One of my fondest memories of my grandmother was her daily phone call. "Soup is ready," she'd say. "Come and get it." Every day, she made a big pot of soup for her family. Her children and grand-children stopped by on their way home from work to pick up their containers or have a quick bowl with whomever was gathered in her kitchen. On those cold winter nights, I looked forward to her soup, yet on the hot summer days I questioned her judgment. But every time I took that first sip of piping hot soup, even on a triple-digit July night, I understood.

For my grandmother, her soup was medicine. Each morning, she looked at the sky and massaged her bones before deciding what kind of soup to make. On hot days, she made seaweed and tofu soup to cool our bodies. If rain threatened, she made oxtail and lotus-root soup to ground us and guard against the dampness. Winter melon soup fortified us against a cold January night. And when my uncle suffered from inflammation in his joints, she made him a special pot of turnip soup to absorb and disperse the heat.

Although my grandmother did not have a day of formal educa-tion to her name, she understood restoring balance through food to be an essential part of maintaining health and curing ailments. This wisdom, passed down through my family for generations, arises from principles developed through the observation and integration of life-cycles found in nature. In East Asian cultures, the Five Elements depict these cycles as water, wood, fire, earth and metal.

Dr. K.C. Liu, my professor of Chinese Philosophy, formally intro-duced me to these principles when I was a college student. I shared my soup stories with him and he remarked, "If you can understand and practice the power of the *Wu Hsing* (the Five Elements) like your grandmother, you can manifest harmony for yourself and for the world."

Balance the relative effects of the elements to maximize their positive effects. That's the key to the Five Elements that, when harnessed properly, bestow health through aligning the Supporting (*sheng*) and Restraining (*ke*) Cycles.

The Supporting (*sheng*) Cycle (**Figure 1**) moves in a clockwise direction. Water nurtures wood, which in turn fuels fire. Fire creates ash or earth, which generates minerals or metal. Finally, metal condenses to form water; while the alchemy between these two elements might not be apparent, put a stainless-steel container in the freezer and watch what happens.

The Restraining (*ke*) Cycle (**Figure 2**) moves across the star formation. Water controls fire, which tempers or melts metal. Metal chops into wood, which depletes the nutrients from the earth. Earth then acts as a container for water.

The Supporting Cycle does not imply "good" and the Restraining Cycle "bad." They are natural processes and, depending on the situation, drawing from one cycle may prove more advantageous. For instance, my grandmother used the Restraining Cycle when she invoked the water qualities of her seaweed soup to cool the fire of the summer day.

Likewise, she referred to the Supporting Cycle by making earth-based turnip soup to draw out the fire of my uncle's inflamed joints.

Figure 3
The Five Elements
Supporting and Restraining Cycles

The Five Elements permeate everything including seasons, colors, shapes, emotions, personality archetypes, flavors and body parts. When it comes to eating for well-being, we focus on flavors, col-

ors, internal organs and external body parts. It might help to keep several reference charts handy in your kitchen and you'll need to spend a few minutes sorting through them before you head out to the grocery store. *First,* note the connections among elements and our bodies charted below:

Figure 4

The Five Elements (major characteristics as they apply to food) [13]

Element	Water	Wood	Fire	Earth	Metal
Color	Blue|Black	Green	Red|Purple	Yellow|Brown	White|Grey
Organ	Kidneys	Liver	Heart	Spleen	Lungs
Body Part	Ears	Mouth	Eyes	Abdomen	Head
Flavor	Salty	Sour	Bitter	Sweet	Pungent

This system connects to a larger practice known as Traditional Chinese Medicine (TCM), that includes acupuncture/acupressure, herbology, massage (*tui na*), movement (*tai chi* and *qi gong*) and culinary alchemy. TCM has been practiced throughout Asia for over 2,500 years and is now an accepted therapy throughout the world. Like medical doctors, TCM practitioners are highly educated, trained and essential in determining treatments based on the particular needs of each person. Remember, for chronic or serious health concerns, consult with your doctor and, if you wish, a practitioner of TCM.

Next, ask yourself who's eating. When in good health, use the Five Elements as a reference to maintain well-being. In order to apply these principles, consider climate and condition.

---

13   Beinfield, Harriet, and Korngold, Efrem, *Between Heaven and Earth: A Guide to Chinese Medicine*, Ballentine Books, 1991.

Figure 5[14]

Climate	Condition
Both Internal and External Hot-Dry Hot-Damp Cold-Dry Cold-Damp	Your general health condition and whether it is chronic, recurring or episodic

Climate is the main contributor in determining the right food. I recently traveled to Cuba, where we experienced hot, damp weather. Fresh fruit such as pineapple, mango and watermelon, along with steamed vegetables and lightly grilled fish, satisfied my need for food that was cooler in nature. However, when I returned to the fog and chill of San Francisco, my cravings turned toward broiled meat and roasted vegetables.

Condition refers to your general health status and whether a health challenge may be chronic, recurring or episodic. Health conditions are aligned with an element and internal organ (e.g. water/kidney, wood/liver, fire/heart, earth/spleen and metal/lungs). Below is a list of some general health conditions and their corresponding elements.

---

14   Pritchard, Paul, *Healing with Whole Foods: Asian Traditions and Modern Nutrition*, North Atlantic Books, 2002.

Figure 6[15]

Element Organ	Water Kidneys	Wood Liver	Fire Heart	Earth Liver	Metal Lungs
Exaggerated Health Conditions (if there is too much of this element in one's system)	Low blood pressure Urinary-tract infections Reproductive issues Depression	Vertigo Migraines Sciatica Hyperactivity	Disorders of the heart and arteries High blood pressure Arrhythmia Insomnia	Indigestion Conjunctivitis Weight management Mood swings	Asthma Eczema or other skin issues Constipation Sinus head-ache
Collapsed Health Conditions (if there is not enough of this element in one's system)	Low energy Osteoporosis Numbness in extremities Dry skin and hair	Tendonitis Hypoglyce-mia Itchy eyes and skin Sensitivity to light or sound	Anemia Low blood pressure Arrhythmia Low energy	Slow healing of cuts Poor muscle tone Swollen glands Mood swings	Incontinence Congested nose, throat and sinus Hair loss Frailty

As with any health condition, remember to seek the counsel of a licensed medical doctor or TCM practitioner. In the case of TCM, the practitioner will look for an imbalance in the elements and determine whether the presence of an element is exaggerated (too strong) or collapsed (too weak). For example, a respiratory disorder may be due to an imbalance of metal in one's system. Treatment will depend on whether there is exaggerated or collapsed metal.

With these two factors—climate and condition—you can develop a diet that aligns with the Five Elements. Through the teachings and observations of my grandmother, I was able to employ these principles intuitively. It may take some practice, but won't take long before you integrate them into your routines.

---

15   Ibid.

While having knowledge of both factors is recommended, it is not required. For instance, you can use the Five Elements based simply on climate. If the day proves to be hot and dry, you may want to prepare foods that use cool and damp methods such as steaming, poaching and stir frying versus smoking, roasting or baking.

Figure 7[16]

Element	Water	Wood	Fire	Earth	Metal
Cooking Method	Boil, steam, poach, cure, freeze, sous vide	Sear, pickle, ferment, smoke, grill	Deep or stir fry, barbeque, sauté, flambé, dehydrate, toast	Bake, roast, stew, mash, puree	Raw constructed foods such as minced, diced or julienne salads, hummus

When choosing foods by the Five Elements, rely on color, flavor and texture. Then employ the various cooking methods above to create the desired meal. Balance is key so try to make sure that all five elements are represented throughout your daily diet, emphasizing one or two elements depending on your constitution, climate and condition. Some examples of foods that you can prepare to enhance or restrict each of the elements may include:

WATER COLOR: BLUE | FLAVOR: SALTY

Water implies a sense of depth, coolness and consolidation. Winter is its season, calling forth qualities of patience and temperance. The kidneys and bladder are the organs related to water. The salty flavor softens and dissolves hard masses. Salty food has a cooling effect and facilitates the movement of energy.

A diet that enhances water includes steamed or lightly grilled seafood, with leafy greens, seaweed, watercress, cucumber and eggplant. Blueberries, blackberries and watermelon are good choices of fruit. Rice and buckwheat are the recommended grains. Using sea

16   Ibid.

salt instead of table salt is an easy way to bring more water into your diet.

If there is excess water in your body, you can balance it with hearty seafood soups and stews, cured or salted food, whole grains, mushrooms, black or kidney beans, and root vegetables such as beets, turnips and burdock.

WOOD COLOR: GREEN | FLAVOR: SOUR

Like the promise of spring, wood is the element of growth and possibility. Following the theme of spring cleaning, it is wise to prepare food that strengthens and cleanses the liver and gallbladder. The flavor of wood is sour (e.g. lemon, vinegar and plum) and acts as an absorbent and astringent. Sour food has a cooling effect and helps the body sort and collect energy.

To enhance wood in your diet, drink plenty of water infused with lemon. Lightly prepared (seared, grilled, smoked) poultry and vegetables such as broccoli, string beans, cabbage, lettuce, summer squash, artichokes and leafy greens marinated in lemon- or vinegar-based sauces are recommended. Eat citrus fruits (e.g. oranges, grapefruits) and pickled food (e.g. sauerkraut, pickles) on a daily basis.

For a person with excess wood, it is helpful to prepare pungent foods—those flavored with garlic, ginger, curry, mustard or miso—to bring a sense of structure and order to the body. Complement with steamed leafy greens or a cucumber salad to bring some lightness into the meal.

FIRE COLOR: RED, PURPLE | FLAVOR: BITTER

Fire represents the peak of summer, when everything reaches its full potential. Vibrancy in food is the key, with bitter flavors accentuating the diverse spices of life. Bitter flavors encourage a drying energy as the fire settles into a foundation of solid ground. This relates to maintaining a vibrant yet calm heart, the organ of fire.

Eating warming foods infused with spices will enhance fire in your diet. Barbequed or stir-fried red meat and vegetables bring the necessary heat to your meal. Consider sautéing bitter greens such as chard, mustard or collard greens, rhubarb and kale with some ginger or garlic. Add tomatoes, beets and pomegranates for color, and amaranth or corn for a grain.

If you have excess fire, employ a water-based diet of steamed or lightly grilled seafood, with leafy greens or cucumber. Add some citrus or vinegar to bring in some wood flavors.

EARTH COLOR: BROWN, YELLOW | FLAVOR: SWEET

The harvest season marks the element of earth. There is a sense of integration as the digestive processes of the spleen and pancreas help to distribute nutrients throughout the body. The sweet flavors harmonize, reinforce and strengthen action toward completion.

Integrated, one-pot meals such as hearty soups and stews help to enhance earth properties. Root vegetables such as yams, sweet potatoes, carrots, parsnips and potatoes contain the grounding needed to sustain bodies. Balance this out with sweet grains such as rice, barley or millet, along with tropical (pineapple, papaya, banana, fig) or late-summer (sweet apples, peaches, pears) fruits.

In cases of excess earth, prepare a wood-based diet of lightly seared or grilled meats and vegetables accompanied by pickled food (slaws or sauerkraut). Complement with bitter greens.

METAL COLOR: WHITE, GREY | FLAVOR: PUNGENT

Metal is associated with autumn, marking the completion of a growing cycle. This element is connected to the lungs and respiratory system. A pungent or *umami* flavor (e.g. garlic, ginger, onions, soy sauce) adds depth and tone to a dish. Like a deep breath, a pungent flavor disperses and equalizes the conditions for a harmonious result.

A diet that enhances metal consists of rich and structured food, with heavier sauces and oils. There is a complexity in the food, as the vegetables tend to be minced, diced or julienne. Salsas and dips (e.g. hummus) are often served with a metal meal. Strong flavors, such as garlic, mustard, cayenne, curry and miso are employed, along with rich textures like tofu, tempeh or fermented cheeses.

For a person with excess metal, add heat with barbequed or stir-fried red meat and vegetables. Add some bitter greens (chard, mustard or collard greens, kale) and finish with some sweet fruit (tropical fruit or sweet apples).

At its core, the Five Elements provide a simple and common-sense framework for us to understand the human condition. Our bodies are, in fact, ecosystems that contain all aspects of the universe. If we can find ways to maintain a sense of harmony within these ecosystems, we can live and eat in more healthy, balanced and beneficial ways.

My grandmother understood these principles and practiced them on a daily basis. In her lifetime, she lived independently and retained her mental acuity, keeping close track of her many grandchildren and great-grandchildren. Her meals, whether a simple pot of soup or nine-course banquet, had aspects of all five elements. She used the Supporting (*sheng*) and Restraining (*ke*) cycles to prepare dishes that responded to the climate of the day, as well as the health conditions and constitutions of her loved ones.

Beyond all the wonderful and balanced meals that she prepared for me, my grandmother was also somewhat of a prophet, for she intuited that the Five Elements would become the foundation for my work as a teacher, healer and cultural translator. The Chinese name she gave to me as a child is *Xi Tang*, which means "Scholar of Soup."

Thanks to her, I not only use the Five Elements to make a good and healthy pot of soup, but I can also create the conditions for communities to bring their collective wisdom together in ways that support and nurture everyone, and there are leftovers to share when they return home.

Figure 8[17]

Element	Water	Wood	Fire	Earth	Metal
Color	Blue/Black	Green	Red/Purple	Yellow/Brown	White/Grey
Organ	Kidneys	Liver	Heart	Spleen	Lungs
Body Part	Eyes	Mouth	Eyes	Abdomen	Head
Flavor	Salty	Sour	Bitter	Sweet	Pungent
Cooking Method	Boil, steam, poach, cure, freeze, sous vide	Sear, pickle, ferment, smoke, grill	Deep or stir fry, barbeque, sauté, flambé, dehydrate, toast	Bake, roast, stew, mash, puree	Raw constructed foods such as minced, diced or julienne salads, hummus
Grains	Buckwheat Rice	Oats Wheat Rye	Amaranth Corn	Millet Barley	Rice
Vegetables	Kale Watercress Seaweed Cucumber Peas	Broccoli Green leafy vegetables Peas Celery Green beans	Chard Mustard greens Collard greens Rhubarb Kale Beets	Carrots Parsnip Rutabaga Spinach Cabbage Squash Potatoes Cauliflower Broccoli	Onion Leek Radish Asparagus Broccoli Celery
Fruit	Blueberries Blackberries Watermelon	Oranges Grapefruit Lemons Limes Plums Avocados Sour apples	Tomatoes, Strawberries Raspberries Pomegranates	Figs Papayas Pineapples Strawberries Sweet apples Peaches Bananas Grapes Cherries	Apricots Bananas Pears

17   Ibid.

Table continued on page 100

Table continued from page 99

Element	Water	Wood	Fire	Earth	Metal
Meat Dairy	Fish Seafood	Poultry Yogurt Kefir White cheese	Red meat Goat cheese Sharp cheese Goat milk	Red meat Poultry Tofu Butter Milk Eggs	Poultry Strong fermented cheese
Legumes Nuts	Kidney Pinto Black Aduki Black sesame Walnut	Green lentil Mung Lima Cashew Brazil	Red lentil	Garbanzo beans Pine nuts Pumpkin seeds	Navy beans Soy beans Almonds
Beverages		Fruit juice Chamomile tea White wine	Green tea Coffee Red wine	Herbal tea Beer Apple juice Grape juice	Peppermint tea Rice wine
Condiments Spices	Salt Seaweed Soy sauce Miso Fish sauce	Vinegar Parsley	Sage Chili Turmeric Oregano Paprika Rosemary Thyme	Cinnamon Anise Vanilla Saffron Maple syrup Honey Raw sugar	Chili Curry Hot sauce Basil Cumin Dill Ginger Cardamom Garlic Mustard

Please note: This chapter is not intended to replace the services of a licensed healthcare provider in the diagnosis or treatment of illness or disease. Any application of the material set forth in the preceding pages is at the reader's discretion and sole responsibility.

MINDFUL MENU

Whole Roasted Chicken ♥ Slaw ♥ Sweet-Potato Bread

BLESSING
(Ashanti [West African] Prayer)

O God, creator of our land,
our earth, the trees, the animals and humans, all is for
your honor.
The drums beat it out, and people sing about it,
and they dance with noisy joy that you are the Lord.

Roasted Chicken | YIELDS 6 PORTIONS

INGREDIENTS

4 cloves of garlic, peeled (2 minced, 2 whole)

2 lemons (zest 1 lemon; cut 1 lemon in half)

1 tbsp dried oregano

1 tsp coarse sea salt

¾ tsp ground black pepper

1 5-lb whole roaster chicken, giblets removed, rinsed and patted dry

½ sweet onion, sliced

1 handful flat-leaf parsley sprigs

DIRECTIONS

1. Preheat oven to 350°F. In a small bowl, combine 2 minced cloves garlic, zest of 1 lemon, oregano, 1 teaspoon salt and ¾ teaspoon pepper.
2. In a roasting pan, place chicken, breast side up. Carefully, without tearing the skin, rub garlic mixture under skin. Place remaining

cloves of garlic, sliced onion, lemon halves and handful of parsley into chicken cavity. Roast, uncovered, for 1 hour, 40 minutes to 1 hour, 50 minutes, or until a thermometer inserted in inner thigh, not touching bone, reads 165°F. Remove from oven, tent with foil and let rest for 10 minutes.

3. Toward end of chicken roasting time, prepare slaw (below). Serve 1½ cups slaw with 5 ounces of chicken.

Slaw | YIELDS 4–6 PORTIONS

INGREDIENTS

4 cups celery, cut into thin short strips

2 carrots, cut into thin short strips

1 apple, cut into thin short strips

¾ cup whole-milk plain yogurt

⅓ avocado, peeled, pitted and mashed

½ cup minced sweet onion

⅓ cup feta cheese

3 tbsp apple cider vinegar

2 tbsp pure maple syrup

1 lemon, zested + 1 tbsp fresh lemon juice

¼ tsp each of sea salt and ground black pepper

½ cup chopped fresh flat-leaf parsley

⅓ cup unsweetened raisins

DIRECTIONS

In a large bowl, combine celeriac, carrots and apple. In a medium bowl, stir together yogurt, avocado, minced onion, cheese, vinegar, maple syrup, lemon zest and juice, and ¼ teaspoon each of salt and pepper. Pour dressing over celeriac mixture and toss well to coat. Stir in chopped parsley and raisins.

Sweet-Potato Bread

INGREDIENTS

2 cups old-fashioned rolled oats

2 tsp ground cinnamon

1 tsp baking powder

1 tsp ground nutmeg

½ tsp baking soda

¼ tsp coarse sea salt

1 large egg

¾ cup whole-milk plain yogurt

5 tbsp pure maple syrup

2 tbsp safflower oil

2 tsp apple-cider vinegar

1 cup peeled, cooked, mashed sweet potatoes, cooled

⅓ cup chopped unsalted walnuts

DIRECTIONS

1. Preheat oven to 350°F. In a blender, pulverize oats into fine flour. In a large bowl, combine oat flour, cinnamon, baking powder, nutmeg, baking soda and salt. In a small bowl, whisk egg; stir in yogurt, maple syrup, oil and vinegar. Add egg mixture to flour mixture; stir until just combined. Fold in potatoes.

2. Line a 9x5 glass loaf pan with parchment paper and mist with cooking spray. Pour batter into loaf pan. Sprinkle walnuts over batter and lightly press down on nuts. Bake for one hour, until a toothpick inserted in center comes out clean. Let cool in pan for 30 minutes; remove and cool completely on a wire rack.

CONTRIBUTOR BIOGRAPHIES

Alex Askew

At age 14, Alex accepted an offer to work as a personal chef. After six years of working in a variety of restaurants in and out of New York City, he enrolled in the Culinary Institute of America and graduated in 1989. With a focus on eating lifestyles and trends in new menu alternatives, he began food research, development and consulting for companies including General Mills, Hilton Hotels, Aramark Corporation, Specialty Restaurants and a host of private clients. He became skilled and knowledgeable in different cooking styles as well as cuisines including Cajun and Creole, holistic, Latin and American fusion. In 1993, Alex cofounded BCA Global (formerly the Black Culinarian Alliance), which dedicates itself to education, awareness and exposure for young minority students seeking careers within the culinary and hospitality industries. He has enjoyed guest appearances on Good Morning America, CBS Early Morning Show and the Food Network. He is a 2001 Doctorate of Foodservice recipient from the North American Foodservice Equipment Manufacturers, a Distinguished Visiting Chef (DVC) for Sullivan University and the 2011 Business Leader of the Year from the Marcella Brown Foundation. In May 2012, Alex received the distinguished New York Institute of Technology Global Leadership Award and serves on the board of the American Culinary Federation. He is also a member of the newly formed Certification and Accreditation Commission. With over 25 years in the restaurant and hospitality fields, Alex continues to use his knowledge and experience as a foundation for further growth and development in the world's best industry.

Anzia Bennett

Anzia is a public-health practitioner committed to health equity and food justice. As the principal of AMB Community Consulting, she works with local health systems, small farmers and community-based organizations to develop wellness programming that is responsive to community-articulated needs, and addresses the social and structural determinants of health. Additionally, she teaches Community Nutrition at the University of New Mexico and leads a monthly series of community cooking classes. For five years, Anzia served as the Food Access program director for the Agri-Cultura Network, a farmer-owned cooperative in Albuquerque's South Valley, where she worked to make locally grown, healthy food affordable and accessible to all. Prior to that, she was the assistant director of Working Classroom, a nonprofit arts and education organization serving young aspiring artists and actors from historically ignored communities in Albuquerque. Anzia received master's degrees in American Studies and Public Health from the University of New Mexico. She serves on the Nurse Family Partnership Community Advisory Board, the Rio Grande Farm Coalition Board of Directors and the Working Classroom Board. She is a W.K. Kellogg Foundation Community Leadership Network Fellow and a Regional Institute for Health and Environmental Leadership Fellow.

Chris Block

Chris is CEO of the American Leadership Forum (ALF) Silicon Valley, a network of 500+ regional leaders committed to serving the common good in Silicon Valley. Through its Fellows program, ALF brings together established leaders to explore the process of collaborative leadership, which can strengthen their capacity to address difficult issues. Graduates of the program—Senior Fellows—develop a common understanding of, dedication to and capacity for acting as networked servant leaders. Chris was himself a Fellow and has deep feelings regarding the power of these fellowships: "My experience as a Fellow strengthened my understanding of how individuals in deep relationships can empower communities to solve their own problems, a framework that I apply every day in my work with community leaders." Prior to ALF, Chris spent 25 years as an affordable-housing developer and nonprofit executive director. He is also a writer, teacher and systems leader. Chris is a longtime Zen practitioner and mindfulness teacher who has taught in settings ranging from corporate training to addiction-recovery programs. He is also a W.K. Kellogg Foundation Fellow.

Jodi Brockington

Jodi is the "judgment-free" fitness and wellness trainer for busy New York City executives. She has developed a signature program, the FOJ 28 Day Challenge, which helps clients to jumpstart and maintain their health and fitness goals. She has been featured in *Our World with Black Enterprise,* the *Black Enterprise Business Report* and *NV Magazine,* among other publications. Some of her most recent work includes serving as deputy director for Speaker Management for the Global Financial Dignity Summit and chief marketing officer for Count Me In for Women's Economic Independence. A sought-after speaker, Jodi has been a presenter at the 2013 Black Enterprise Women of Power Summit, and presented a crash course on how to connect effectively and with confidence at the 2014 Summit. Her awards and honors include a Beauty & Beat Award, a 2012 Heroines of Excellence Award, an *NV Magazine* 2011 Mover and Shaker Award, *The Network Journal* "40 Under 40" Award and an Urban Influencer Award from the National Urban League. Jodi has been featured in print publications and digital media such as *TrendSetters Magazine, Racing Towards Diversity Magazine, NV Magazine,* The BOSS Network and NV.com. She earned master's degrees from the University of Southern California in social work, Baruch College in public affairs and from the Hunter College School of Education. She completed her undergraduate studies at the University of California, Los Angeles (UCLA).

Michael S. Easterling

Michael is a social entrepreneur with nearly 20 years of experience in nonprofit capacity building. His core services include strategic planning, program development and project management for new initiatives and early-stage ventures. Michael's work in urban agriculture and local food-systems development started when he began cultivating an organic garden in 2006. In the process of growing it from 400 square feet to more than 4,000 over the course of three seasons, he began to network with the well-established local food movement in Cleveland, OH. Michael currently chairs the academics committee of Farm School NYC, a two-year certificate program in urban agriculture funded by the USDA New Farmer/New Rancher grant. He is also the conference-committee chair of Black Urban Growers (BUGs), a community-based group in NYC that annually produces the national Black Farmers & Urban Gardeners conference. In addition to organizing and convening, he also teaches a course in sustainable food-system development with Garden State Urban Farms, a network of commercial greenhouses that sells directly to restaurants in the Tri-State Area, and partners with Essex County College to implement a workforce-development program in urban agriculture.

Kevin Fong

Kevin is a nationally recognized and respected facilitator, trainer and speaker in leadership, executive development, organizational systems, philosophy and design. He has extensive experience working with clients in the public and private sectors, especially with diverse multicultural and multilingual groups. He serves as lead faculty in several leadership-training programs and fellowships; facilitates board, executive and team-building retreats; coaches corporate and nonprofit executive leaders; and plans and facilitates seminars and conferences on governance and leadership. Prior to creating his consulting practice Elemental Partners in 1995, Kevin spent five years in executive management at Macy's CA, and eight years directing a clinical HIV program and teen clinic at Asian Health Services, a community health center in Oakland, CA. In addition, he was awarded a three-year fellowship from the W.K. Kellogg Foundation. He has served on numerous community and national boards, and has played a key role in the development of several social-service organizations in the San Francisco Bay Area. A third-generation Asian-Pacific American, Kevin earned bachelor's degrees in Physiology and East Asian Studies at the University of California, Berkeley.

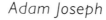

Adam Joseph

Born in Groton, CT, Adam was raised in Champaign, IL, where he attended private schools, participated in numerous athletics and was the only child of a single mother. Her dedication as a parent and perseverance as a mentor helped Adam earn the Eagle Scout and Order of the Arrow, receive a congressional appointment to West Point, and develop a passion for good food. He began his professional career in youth development, working in the Champaign-Urbana public school system as an inclusion aide, and directing YMCA summer camps. He transitioned to the food and hospitality industries as a head chef during the Jacob's Pillow Dance Festival in the Berkshires, MA, and a three-month international co-op in Newport, South Wales, at the Celtic Manor Hotel and Resort. Adam received his bachelor's degree in Foodservice Management from Johnson & Wales University and an MBA in Hospitality with a concentration in Event Leadership, and is currently a culinary instructor at Kennesaw State University in Kennesaw, GA. He is an enthusiastic addition to the Michael Leven School of Culinary Sustainability and Hospitality College, and a single father of three children.

Njathi Kabui

Njathi is an organic chef based in Durham, NC, whose personal history, education and experience have given him a unique perspective on food. Born in Kenya, his most direct connection to food is through his father, who owned a restaurant in the city of Nairobi. His mother was a coffee farmer and also grew some of the family's food. It is from her that Njathi learned the true cost of good food as well as the valuable skill of growing it. He is committed to continuing this rich legacy by sharing his experience and recipes as he travels across the country and beyond. After high school, Njathi attended LeMoyne-Owen College in Memphis, TN, where he studied Political Science and Philosophy. He then proceeded to the University of Memphis, earning a dual master's degree in Medical Anthropology and Urban Anthropology. He worked in the field of food activism for several years before enrolling in culinary school at the Center of Green Studies in Pittsboro, NC. He then formed the group Organics & Sounds (www.organicsandsounds.com) that works to empower people with the skills necessary to improve the food system, health and the environment. He speaks and hosts dinners across the country to raise funds for his work in both the U.S. and Kenya, preparing his famous and eclectic dinners for a diverse array of guests and venues. He was also recently invited to be a guest chef at the Kenyan Embassy in Washington, DC, and at some of the best wineries east of Mississippi. He is an avid gardener and grows a variety of organic food.

Brealynn Lee

Brealynn has been in the culinary business for 15 years. An artist in her own right, she studied graphic design at the Art Institute of Dallas on a scholarship and graduated in 2002. She returned to the Art Institute to study in their new culinary program after a close friend there inspired her to explore another form of art: "I fell in love with art all over again when I started culinary." And why not? She has been cooking since age 4, using a chair to climb onto the countertop in her grandmother's kitchen in Mississippi. With hard work and determination, Brealynn obtained three degrees in culinary and pastry from Le Cordon Bleu. She is an executive culinary chef and executive pastry chef specializing in chocolate. In 2010, she became the second student of the Texas chapter of BCA Global (Black Culinarian Alliance) and, upon graduation in 2012 from Le Cordon Bleu, became the first alumni president. She has continued to educate and mentor young minority chefs in the industry's ways and protocol, and believes that we can change the world one meal at a time.

Veronica McLymont, PhD, RDN, CDN

Veronica is a registered and certified dietitian/nutritionist, and the director of Food and Nutrition Services at Memorial Sloan Kettering Cancer Center in New York. She holds a bachelor's degree in Food and Nutrition from Brooklyn College, a master's degree in Nutrition from Hunter College, and a doctorate in Organizational Leadership from the University of Maryland Eastern Shore.

Veronica has taught as an adjunct professor in a master's program at Hunter College, is a past president of the Association for Healthcare Foodservice (New York chapter), and a past president of the Westchester Rockland Dietetic Association. She is a longtime partner with American Corporate Partners (ACP), a national nonprofit, where she provides year-long mentorship to returning veterans as they transition into the civilian workforce.

In 2008, Veronica was voted a "Trend Setter" by the American Society for Healthcare Food Service Administrators. In 2011, she was recognized as one of the "25 Most Influential Black Women in Business" by *The Network Journal.* In 2017 she was listed among the Top Women in Metro New York Foodservice and Hospitality by *Total Foodservice* magazine. In 2013, Veronica received the Isabelle A. Hallahan Award for Excellence in Food Service from the New York State Dietetic Association. In 2015, she received the Excellence in Management Practice award from the Academy of Nutrition and Dietetics, and in 2016 received the Exemplary Leadership award from the Association for Healthcare Foodservice. Veronica is coauthor of a chapter in the textbook *Research: Successful Approaches,* and author of the chapter "Nutrition Care of the Cancer Patient" in a cancer-rehabilitation textbook. She has coauthored several research articles, given numerous lectures on nutrition and leadership-related topics, and is sought after as a food and nutrition resource.

Claude E. Nunn III

Claude is the president of Nunn Better Nutrition and has been a certified executive/working chef for 45 years throughout the United States and internationally, with extensive experience in diners, dinner houses, high-end restaurants, four- and five-star resorts, hotels and private clubs. Within those venues, guests have included heads of state, celebrities, corporate executives and U.S. presidents from Reagan to Obama. Claude graduated from California Culinary Academy in San Francisco and an immersion program at the Institute of Integrative Nutrition in New York. His culinary, nutrition, wellness, cross-fit and urban-farming training, experience and education have led him to develop and deliver a three-in-one wellness concept and healthy-lifestyle model that helps people to help themselves. Claude's philosophy as a wellness chef is a model of ancient, old-world and rebirthed theories and practices encompassing body, soul and spirit. He uses this model version of creation, consciousness and conception to lead people to a better understanding of the benefits of mindful and conscious eating, and an awareness of the power of superfoods. Spiritual awareness and earthly elements produce a healthier, stronger and more intuitive body.

Elizabeth Michaelle Rinehart

Elizabeth Michaelle Rinehart is a citizen of the Pokagon Band of Potawatomi Indians, a woodland tribe of the Southern Michigan/Northern Indiana region. She currently teaches at the Huron Potawatomi Head Start program. Elizabeth attends Grand Valley State University as a graduate student, majoring in curriculum and instruction with a HS endorsement for early childhood. Elizabeth weaves traditional language, songs and stories into outdoor lessons as a way to revitalize the Potawatomi culture. Prior to Huron Potawatomi Head Start, Elizabeth co-facilitated project Kit-ta-gin, a food-sovereignty program through the W.K. Kellogg Foundation. This project is aimed at empowering vulnerable children and their families via improved access to healthier food through gardening. She also has been a recipient of the Neighborhood Match Fund grant from the City of Grand Rapids. Elizabeth's work with Kit-ta-gin has been published in *Native Head Start Leadership Quarterly*.

Jonathan Rinehart, Sr.

Jonathan is an alumnus of the W.K. Kellogg Foundation Community Leadership Network and Grand Valley State University School of Social Work, and is a case manager for the Behavioral Health Department of the Nottawaseppi Huron Band of the Potawatomi Tribe. Prior to his current position, Jonathan worked as the NHBP's northern youth specialist. During his time there, he demonstrated his care and concern for tribal youth, recognizing the importance of sharing knowledge and resources to the next generation. He has been doing this work for over 15 years for urban Native Americans living in the Greater Grand Rapids area. One of Jonathan's many gifts is raising awareness about issues concerning the community and then working to bring forth solutions. He served as chair for Anishinaabe Circle, an emerging nonprofit organization focused on bridging service gaps within communities. As a strong advocate for food sovereignty and food justice in the urban Native American community, his latest project focused on improving access to healthier food options, encouraging community participants to grow their own food through the installation of raised-bed gardens, followed by instructions on how to care for the plants until harvest. Jonathan continues to advocate for food justice as a mechanism to empower vulnerable children and their families.

Victor A. Ruiz

Victor is the executive director of Esperanza, Inc., with a mission to improve the academic achievement of Hispanics in Greater Cleveland by supporting students to graduate from high school and promoting postsecondary educational attainment in the Hispanic community. As a result of Esperanza's efforts, the high-school graduation rate of Cleveland's Hispanic youth has doubled since 2010. The organization has received local and national recognition for its work, including being named a 2015 Bright Spot in Hispanic Education by the White House Initiative on Educational Excellence for Hispanics, and receiving the prestigious Anisfield-Wolf Community Organization Award from the Cleveland Foundation in 2012. Victor lives in Cleveland with his wife and three children, and is a graduate of the Cleveland school system. He has a bachelor's degree in English from Baldwin Wallace College and a master's in education from Cleveland State University. He serves on several boards and committees in leadership roles, including chairman of the board of Cuyahoga Community College and of the Hispanic Alliance. Victor is also a W.K. Kellogg Foundation National Fellow.

CPSIA information can be obtained
at www.ICGtesting.com
Printed in the USA
FFOW04n1846030118
44339628-43993FF

9 781938 798177